Emma Poole • Caroline Reynolds • Bob Wo

ESSENTIALS

Year 8
KS3 Science
Coursebook

How to Use this Coursebook

A Note to the Teacher

This is the second of three science coursebooks for students in Key Stage 3.

Together, the coursebooks for Years 7, 8 and 9 provide full coverage of the programme of study for Key Stage 3 science.

Each coursebook comprises...
- clear, concise content appropriate to that year
- questions and tasks to reinforce students' learning and help improve their confidence.

This Year 8 coursebook is split into 12 topics. The topics are colour-coded to show which of the following headings they come under:
- Life Processes, Responses and Survival (green)
- Elements, Compounds and Rocks (red)
- Heat, Magnetism, Light and Sound (blue).

Each topic consists of seven pages.

The first four pages of a topic contain the content students need to learn. They feature...
- **key words** picked out in colour in the text and listed in a box at the end of each topic
- a **Quick Test** to test understanding.

The final three pages in a topic contain questions and exercises to reinforce students' understanding and provide skills practice:
- **Key Words Exercise** – requires students to match the key words to their definitions.
- **Comprehension** – requires students to answer questions based on a passage that explores the nature, history and understanding of the scientific ideas introduced in the topic.
- **Testing Understanding** – comprises a literacy exercise, and another exercise to develop skills such as the interpretation of graphs and data.
- **Skills Practice** – devoted to a relevant investigation to develop the students' investigative skills. The students can just answer the questions, or carry out the investigation before answering the questions.

A pull-out answer book, which contains the answers to all the questions in this coursebook, is included.

Each coursebook is supported by a workbook to provide further practice and help consolidate students' learning.

A Note to the Student

We're sure you'll enjoy using this coursebook, but follow these helpful hints to make the most of it:
- Try to learn what all the key words mean.
- The tick boxes on the contents page let you track your progress: simply put a tick in the box next to each topic when you're confident that you know it.
- Try to write your answers in good English, using correct punctuation and good sentence construction. Read what you have written to make sure it makes sense.
- Think carefully when drawing graphs. Always make sure you have accurately labelled your axes and that you have plotted points accurately.

Contents

Food and Life

What is Life?

Life is being able to fulfil a series of processes that can be remembered by 'Mrs Gren':

- **M**ovement.
- **R**espiration (release of energy).
- **S**ensitivity.
- **G**rowth.
- **R**eproduction.
- **E**xcretion (removal of waste products).
- **N**utrition.

To be considered alive, an organism must be able to carry out all these processes.

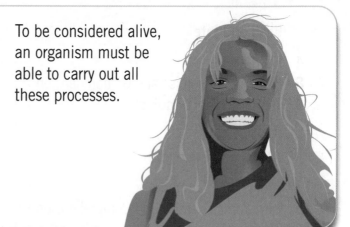

Humans as Living Organisms

Each cell in a living organism has a specialised job. Cells are arranged in tissues, which make up organs. Organs work together as a system, and systems make up the whole organism to enable it to live.

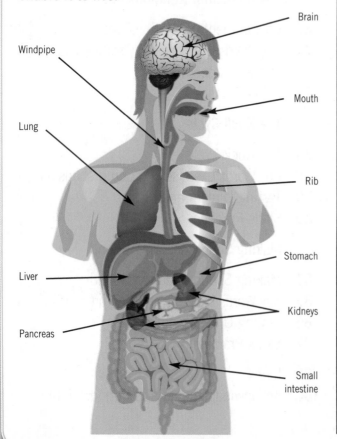

Process	Organs Involved	Systems
Movement	Muscles and skeleton	Skeletal and musculature
	Blood vessels transport materials around the body	Circulatory
Respiration	All cells respire, but lungs and windpipe are needed for breathing	Respiratory (or pulmonary)
Sensitivity	Brain; spinal cord; nerves	Nervous
Growth	Cells and organs	All
Reproduction	Male – penis; testes Female – ovaries; uterus; vagina	Reproductive
Excretion	Kidneys; liver; skin; lungs	Excretory
Nutrition	Mouth; stomach; intestines	Digestive

How Food is Used

Your body mainly needs food for...
- energy
- growth
- repair.

You need to have the right amount of each of the seven food types (nutrients) for your individual needs. This is called a **balanced diet**.

Along with enough exercise, a balanced diet will help you to stop becoming overweight and unhealthy.

A baby needs a lot of food for growth, especially for bones and teeth.

An old man needs less food as he's not so active.

An active child needs a lot of food for energy and growth.

Food Types

Nutrient	Needed for...	Found in...
Carbohydrates (starches and sugars)	energy	potatoes; bread; fruit; cereals
Proteins	growth and repair of body tissues	meat; fish; eggs; nuts
Vitamins	helping processes in your body work efficiently, e.g. vitamin D for bone development	citrus fruit; fresh vegetables
Minerals	helping to produce body chemicals and materials, e.g. iron for blood; calcium for teeth and bones	milk; fresh vegetables; fruit
Fats and oils	energy and insulation	milk; butter; cheese; olives
Fibre (roughage)	helping to push food through the body. It's not digested but prevents many bowel problems	wholemeal bread; bran; fresh vegetables; fruit
Water	all processes in your body, which is why you're made up of about 70% water	all foods and, of course, you can drink it!

Food and Life

The Digestive System

The digestive system breaks down the large, insoluble molecules in carbohydrates, proteins and fats into small, soluble molecules that can be absorbed into the blood through the intestine wall. This process is called **digestion**.

Vitamins, minerals and water are already small enough to pass through the intestine wall, so they don't need to be broken down.

The heart pumps blood around the body so that cells can get the food materials they need.

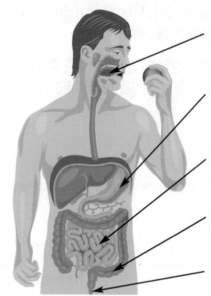

In the mouth, food is ground up and mixed with saliva.

The stomach contains acid to kill bacteria and some protein is broken down here. Food stays here for 2–3 hours.

In the intestines, food is broken down and absorbed into the blood to be taken to the cells that need it.

Undigested food (fibre) is stored for a while...

...until it's removed from the body through the anus as faeces. This is called egestion.

Enzymes

The body produces chemicals called **enzymes** that break down the large molecules into small ones so they can be absorbed into the blood.

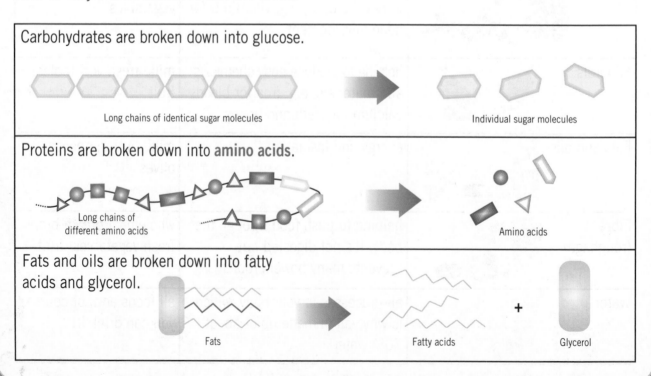

Carbohydrates are broken down into glucose.

Long chains of identical sugar molecules

Individual sugar molecules

Proteins are broken down into **amino acids**.

Long chains of different amino acids

Amino acids

Fats and oils are broken down into fatty acids and glycerol.

Fats

Fatty acids

+

Glycerol

Photosynthesis

Photosynthesis is the process that green plants use to get their food. It involves...

- plants using the energy from sunlight to turn **carbon dioxide** from the air, and water from the soil, into glucose in the leaf
- oxygen being released into the air as a waste product.

| carbon dioxide | + | water | sunlight → | glucose | + | oxygen |

The leaves carry out photosynthesis. They're thin, have a large surface area and are arranged on a branch to get as much light as possible.

The palisade cells are packed with chloroplasts that contain the green pigment, **chlorophyll**, which absorbs the light energy for the plant.

Carbon dioxide is taken from the air through the stomata (pores in the lower epidermis). Water is taken from the soil by root-hair cells and then taken up the stem to the leaf.

The glucose is usually stored as starch in the leaves where it can be used...

- in respiration to release energy for the plant
- to make new cellulose for cell walls
- to make starch for storage in roots or tubers
- to make protein for growth (this needs elements from the soil, such as **nitrogen** and phosphorus, taken in by root-hair cells)
- to make oils for storage in seeds or fruits.

The waste oxygen is released to the air from the stomata.

Photosynthesis is very important. Without it, there would be no food or oxygen.

Leaf Structure

Waxy cuticle
Upper epidermis
Palisade layer
Spongy mesophyll
Lower epidermis
Guard cell
Stomata
Veins

A Root-hair Cell

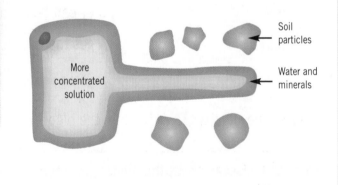

Soil particles
More concentrated solution
Water and minerals

Quick Test

1. Name three processes that all living things must do.
2. The nervous system consists of which three parts?
3. Which food type isn't digested but helps food move through the digestive system?
4. What is the name of the green pigment in plants?

KEY WORDS

Make sure you understand these words before moving on!

- Amino acids
- Balanced diet
- Carbon dioxide
- Chlorophyll
- Digestion
- Enzymes
- Fibre
- Nitrogen
- Photosynthesis
- Protein

Food and Life

Key Words Exercise

Match each key word with its meaning.

Amino acids	A substance in the diet used for growth and repair of body tissues
Balanced diet	The process by which plants make food
Carbon dioxide	The green pigment that absorbs light energy
Chlorophyll	An element necessary for plants to make protein
Digestion	Helps push food through the intestine and prevents bowel problems
Enzymes	The small molecules produced after protein digestion
Fibre	Chemicals that break down large, insoluble molecules into small, soluble molecules
Nitrogen	Contains the right proportions of the seven food types for you
Photosynthesis	The breakdown of large food molecules into small molecules so they can be absorbed
Protein	A gas that plants need in order to photosynthesise

Comprehension

Read the passage about the model gut, then answer the following questions.

Amylase is an enzyme that breaks down starch into sugar. It's found in saliva. In the experiment shown, some starch solution and amylase were placed in Visking tubing, which was sealed at one end and placed in a beaker of water. Samples of the contents of the tubing were taken every 30 seconds and tested for starch and sugar. Similarly, samples of the water around the tubing were taken every 30 seconds and also tested for starch and sugar. The results showed that sugar appeared in the water outside the tubing after one minute but starch never appeared. Inside the tubing, the solution tested positive for starch immediately and positive for sugar after 30 seconds. However, after three minutes and 30 seconds the contents of the tubing no longer tested positive for starch.

1. Which part of the digestive system is the Visking tubing supposed to represent?

2. Why was there no sugar at first inside the tubing?

3. Which part of the human body is the water in the beaker supposed to represent?

4. What caused sugar to appear in the tubing?

5. Why did sugar appear in the water outside the tubing but starch didn't appear?

6. Why did the starch inside the tubing eventually disappear?

7. How does the experiment compare with what happens in the human gut?

Testing Understanding

1 **Fill in the missing words to complete the sentences about food and life.**

a) A _____ diet provides the appropriate amounts of all _____

major food types.

b) You need _____ and fats for energy. You need _____ for

growth and repair of tissues. Minerals and _____ are needed in very small

amounts to help your body work well and keep you healthy.

c) If you eat too much food and don't do enough exercise, you may become

_____. You need quite a lot of _____ in your diet as

70% of your body is made up of it.

d) Digestion breaks down large _____ into smaller ones using chemicals

called _____. This means that food is easily _____ through

the intestine wall and into the _____, which carries it to where it's needed.

e) Plants don't eat food from the soil but make their own by _____. The gas,

_____, from the air, and _____

from the soil, are turned into glucose using energy from _____. This

process also releases _____ into the air as a waste product.

2 **Read the information provided, then answer the questions that follow.**

The table opposite shows the energy requirements of seven different people.

a) Plot this data as a bar chart on graph paper.
b) Suggest why the 21-year-old man needs more energy than the 21-year-old woman?
c) Explain the difference in energy needs between the two 35-year-old men.
d) Explain why the woman who is pregnant needs more energy than the other woman.

Person	Energy Needs per Day (kJ)
6-year-old child	7 000
14-year-old boy	15 500
21-year-old man	13 500
21-year-old woman	11 000
21-year-old pregnant woman	12 500
35-year-old male clerical worker	12 500
35-year-old male manual worker	19 000

Food and Life

Phil and Cherry decided to investigate the effect of light intensity on the rate of photosynthesis in Canadian pondweed.

They set up the experiment as shown and recorded their results in the table below.

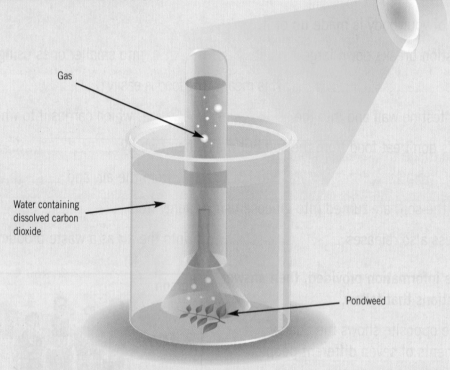

Gas

Water containing dissolved carbon dioxide

Pondweed

Distance from Lamp (cm)	10	20	30	40	50	60	80	100
Amount of Gas Collected in 10 minutes (cm³)	100	75	65	50	30	15	15	15

1. Plot the data onto a graph grid, labelling the axes clearly.

2. What gas would you expect to collect in the tube?

3. What conclusion can you draw from this graph?

4. How much gas would be collected at:
   a) 25cm?
   b) 120cm?

5. Which is the dependent variable (the variable that's being measured) in this investigation?

6. Why do you think the amount of gas didn't change between 60cm and 100cm?

7. Which key variables would need to be carefully controlled in order to make this a fair test?

Atoms and Elements

Materials

Everything around us is made from different materials. This car is made from lots of different materials.

Different materials have different properties. The material you choose for a particular job depends on many factors including the properties you need, the cost and availability.

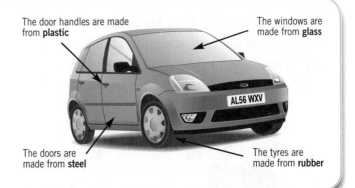

The door handles are made from **plastic**

The windows are made from **glass**

The doors are made from **steel**

The tyres are made from **rubber**

AL56 WXV

Elements

Materials are made from very small particles called **atoms**. Some materials are special because they only contain one type of atom. These materials are called **elements**.

Water pipes are often made from copper. Copper is an element because it only contains copper atoms. The atoms have a regular arrangement so it's a solid.

There are only about 100 different elements. They're displayed in the **periodic table**.

Saucepans are often made from steel. Steel isn't an element. It's a mixture of iron, carbon and chromium. Mixtures of metals are called **alloys**.

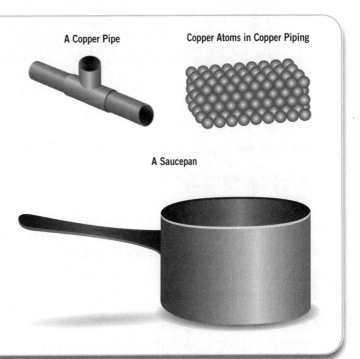

A Copper Pipe

Copper Atoms in Copper Piping

A Saucepan

Inside Atoms

Atoms are made up of three types of particles:
*   Protons.
*   Neutrons.
*   Electrons.

Protons and neutrons are found in the nucleus of the atom. The number of protons in an atom is called the **atomic number**.

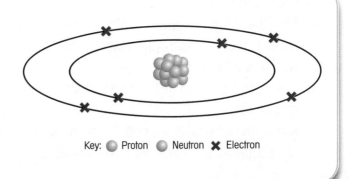

Key: Proton   Neutron ✖ Electron

Atoms and Elements

The Periodic Table

Russian scientist Dimitri Mendeleev designed the periodic table, which places the elements into a meaningful order. The elements are arranged in order of increasing atomic number.

This means that elements with similar properties are in the same column or 'group'. The table also splits the elements into metals and non-metals.

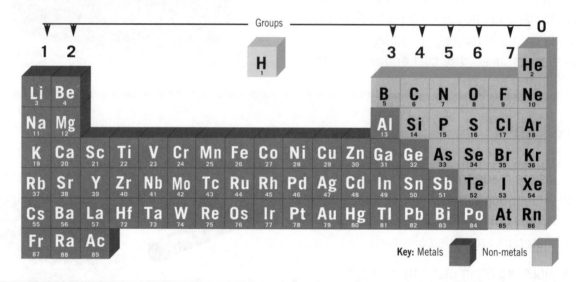

Metals and Non-Metals

The metal elements are found on the left-hand side of the periodic table. More than three-quarters of the elements are metals and they include aluminium, iron and copper.

Metals have these characteristic properties:
- They're shiny, especially when freshly cut.
- They're hard and strong.
- They're dense (heavy for their size).
- They're good conductors of heat and electricity.
- They have high melting points so they're solid at room temperature (except mercury, which is a liquid).
- They can be drawn into wire and hammered into shape.
- A few metals (e.g. iron, cobalt and nickel) are magnetic but most are non-magnetic.

The non-metal elements are found on the right-hand side of the periodic table. Less than a quarter of the elements are non-metals and they include helium, oxygen and carbon.

Non-metals have these characteristic properties:
- They have a low density (are light for their size).
- They're poor conductors of heat and electricity (except carbon in the form of graphite, which is a good electrical conductor).
- They have lower melting points so many are gases (e.g. nitrogen) at room temperature. A few are solid (e.g. sulfur). Only bromine is a liquid.

Symbols

Scientists use **symbols** to represent different elements. In some cases, the symbol is simply the first letter of the element's name.

In other cases, where several elements start with the same letter, the symbol is the first letter of the element's name followed by another letter from its name. When two letters are used...

- the first letter is a capital letter
- the second letter is lower case.

Sometimes the symbol comes from the Latin name.

Element	Symbol
Carbon	C
Nitrogen	N
Oxygen	O
Calcium	Ca
Chlorine	Cl

Element	Latin Name	Symbol
Iron	ferrum	Fe
Sodium	natrium	Na

Compounds

A **compound**...

- is a substance formed when the atoms of two or more different elements are joined together by a chemical reaction
- has very different properties from the elements it was made from.

Molecules

A **molecule** is formed when a small group of atoms are joined together.

The atoms can be the same (e.g. hydrogen) or different (e.g. carbon dioxide).

Dalton's Symbols

The scientist John Dalton used different symbols to represent atoms.

 Oxygen Carbon Hydrogen Sulfur

This diagram represents an element (carbon). The atoms are close together and are in a regular arrangement, so this is solid carbon. 	This diagram represents a compound (sulfur dioxide). Each sulfur atom is joined to two oxygen atoms. The molecules are far apart, so this is sulfur dioxide gas.
This diagram shows molecules of an element (oxygen). The molecules are far apart, so this is oxygen gas. 	This diagram also represents a compound (water). Each oxygen atom is joined to two hydrogen atoms. The molecules are far apart, so this is water vapour.

Atoms and Elements

Reactants and Products

During a chemical reaction, new substances are made. The chemicals present at the start of the reaction are called the **reactants**.

The new substances made by the reaction are called the **products**. Here are two examples:

① Hydrogen and Oxygen	② Carbon and Oxygen
When hydrogen is burned, it reacts with oxygen to form water vapour. Hydrogen and oxygen are the reactants; water is the product.	When carbon is burned in a good supply of oxygen, a chemical reaction takes place and carbon dioxide is made.

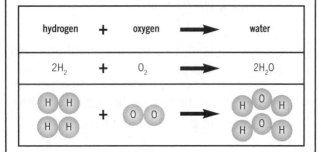

hydrogen	+	oxygen	→	water
$2H_2$	+	O_2	→	$2H_2O$

carbon	+	oxygen	→	carbon dioxide
C	+	O_2	→	CO_2

Metal Oxides

Most metals react if they're heated in air. The metal reacts with the oxygen in air to form a metal **oxide**. Metals burn more vigorously in pure oxygen than they do in air. This is the reaction between magnesium and oxygen:

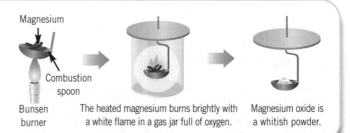

Magnesium

Combustion spoon

Bunsen burner

The heated magnesium burns brightly with a white flame in a gas jar full of oxygen.

Magnesium oxide is a whitish powder.

Quick Test

1. What is special about an element?
2. How are elements arranged in the periodic table?
3. An element is solid, conducts electricity and is shiny when freshly cut. What does this tell you about the element?
4. Identify the element from the symbol...
   a) C **b)** O **c)** Ca **d)** Fe
5. Name the product made when magnesium metal is burned in air.

KEY WORDS

Make sure you understand these words before moving on!

- Alloy
- Atom
- Atomic number
- Compound
- Element
- Molecule
- Oxide
- Periodic table
- Product
- Reactant
- Symbol

Key Words Exercise

Match each key word with its meaning.

Key word	Meaning
Alloy	A material that's made of only one type of atom
Atom	A very small particle
Atomic number	A way of displaying elements in order of increasing atomic number
Compound	A mixture of metals
Element	A one or two-letter code used to represent an element
Molecule	Contains atoms of two or more different elements that have been joined together by a chemical reaction
Oxide	A small group of atoms that are joined together
Periodic table	The chemical used up during a reaction
Product	The number of protons in an atom
Reactant	The substance made by a chemical reaction
Symbol	Made when a material is burned in air

Comprehension

Read the passage about Dimitri Mendeleev and the periodic table, then answer the following questions.

1. Where was Dimitri Mendeleev born?

2. In which city did Mendeleev study science?

3. How did Mendeleev become famous?

4. How many elements were known when Mendeleev designed his table?

5. Why did he leave gaps in his table?

6. Why didn't Mendeleev include any noble gases in his table?

7. Which element was named after Mendeleev?

8. What else was named after Mendeleev?

Dimitri Mendeleev was born in Siberia in 1834. He was the youngest of at least 14 children. After his father died and his mother's glass factory burned down, the family moved to St. Petersburg. Mendeleev studied science at the university and eventually became a professor.

Mendeleev became famous for designing the first version of the periodic table. He placed the 63 known elements in order of increasing atomic weight. He left spaces and used his table to make detailed predictions about the properties of the missing elements. When the elements were eventually discovered and their properties closely matched Mendeleev's predictions, he proved that the table was a powerful way of helping us to understand the world around us.

Mendeleev also changed the order of the elements occasionally so that elements with similar properties were placed in the same vertical column or group. This meant that Mendeleev had actually placed the elements in order of increasing atomic number. Mendeleev's table looked a little different from the modern periodic table. For example, he didn't include any noble gases as they hadn't been discovered and many scientists have made improvements to his original ideas.

Today, more than 100 years after his death, Mendeleev is famous all over the world. The radioactive element 101 was named mendelevium and the Mendeleev crater on the Moon was named after him.

Atoms and Elements

1 **Fill in the missing words to complete the sentences about atoms and elements.**

a) Everything around us is made of small particles called _____. Some materials are made of only one type of atom and these materials are called _____.

b) There are about 100 different elements and they're often arranged in the _____ table. The elements can be split into metals and _____-metals. The metals are found on the _____-hand side of the periodic table.

c) Metals are hard and _____, especially when they're freshly cut. Only one metal isn't solid at room temperature. This metal is called _____ and is used in thermometers.

d) Non-metals are poor conductors of both heat and _____. Oxygen is a non-metal element. When magnesium is heated in air, it reacts with _____ to produce magnesium _____.

2 **Study the diagrams, then answer the questions that follow.**

These symbols represent atoms:

These diagrams show different combinations of these atoms:

A	B	C	D

a) Give the letters of the diagrams that show elements.
b) Give the letter of the diagram that shows a solid.
c) Give the letter of the diagram of an element that's a gas.
d) Give the letters of the diagrams that show compounds.

Duncan wants to investigate what happened to the mass of magnesium metal when it was burned in oxygen.

1 Complete the word equation to sum up the reaction between magnesium and oxygen.

magnesium + oxygen ➡ ....

2 Duncan measured the mass of the magnesium at the start of the reaction and the mass of the product at the end of the reaction. The results are shown in the table below.

a) Complete the table by adding the units at the top of the last column.
b) Calculate the difference in mass and write this in the last column of the table.

3 a) Use the information in the table to complete the graph below.
b) Add a line of best fit.
c) Use the graph to write a conclusion for the experiment.

Mass of Magnesium Burned (g)	Mass of the Magnesium After it's Burned (g)	Difference in Mass
0.6	1.0	0.4
1.2	2.0	
1.8	3.5	
2.4	4.0	

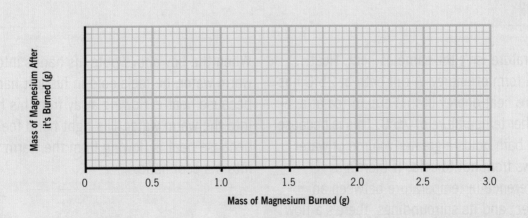

Getting Hotter, Getting Colder

Temperature

Humans aren't good judges of **temperature**. The boy opposite has his left hand in hot water and his right hand in cold water. When he puts both hands into the bowl of warm water, his left hand feels cold and his right hand feels warm.

The hotness or coldness of something is measured by taking its temperature.

The unit of temperature is **degrees Celsius** or °C.

You can measure temperature accurately using a **thermometer**:

- Galileo invented the first thermometer in 1600 based on the expansion of air.
- In the 1700s, Daniel Fahrenheit, a German scientist, invented a better thermometer using expanding mercury in a glass tube. His unit for temperature was the degree Fahrenheit.
- The Celsius scale of temperature is named after Anders Celsius, a Swedish scientist. His scale placed melting ice at 0 and boiling water at 100, which made it easier for people to make a thermometer.

COLD WATER WARM WATER HOT WATER

Heat

Temperature isn't the same as **heat**. Heat…

- is a form of energy. A full bath at 25°C has more heat energy than a cup of tea at a higher temperature of 75°C. This is because the bath holds a greater volume of water
- flows from hot to cold. If there's a difference in temperature between an object and its surroundings, there's a flow of heat from hot to cold.

When the boy above puts his hands into the warm water, he feels cold in his left hand because heat is flowing away from his hot hand into the warm water. His right hand feels warm because heat is flowing from the warm water into his cool hand.

Conduction

Heat travels through solids by a process called **conduction**. If you stir hot soup with a metal spoon, the heat quickly flows through the metal from the soup to your hand. Metal is a good conductor because heat can flow easily through it. As the particles in the solid vibrate, the heat energy is passed along.

If you stir the hot soup with a wooden or a plastic spoon, the heat can't travel so easily to your hand. Wood and plastic aren't good conductors of heat; they're called **insulators**.

A stone floor will feel colder to your bare feet than a carpet because...
- stone is a good conductor of heat and the heat flows quickly from your feet into the stone
- a carpet is an insulator and doesn't conduct the heat away from your feet quickly.

Convection

Heat can travel through liquids and gases:
- In a kettle, only the water at the bottom of the kettle is heated but the heat travels through all the water until it boils.
- When a room is heated using a radiator, only the air next to the radiator is heated but the heat travels until all of the room is heated.

Liquids and gases are poor conductors of heat. Heat travels through them another way, by **convection**.

Convection...
- is when the particles in a liquid or a gas move, carrying the heat with them from one place to another
- can't happen in solid objects because the particles aren't free to move from one place to another.

The movement of the air around a room is called a convection current. Hot air carries the heat and the cooler air travels back towards the heat source.

Getting Hotter, Getting Colder

More About Convection

Hot air expands, making it less dense and therefore lighter than cold air. Hot liquids are also lighter than cold liquids. This means that hot air or liquid rises:

- Hot-air balloons rise.
- In a kettle, the water at the bottom is heated. It becomes lighter and moves upwards. The cold water takes its place next to the element and heats up.
- In a fridge, the cooling element is placed at the top. The air is cooled by the element and sinks to the bottom of the fridge because it's heavier. The hotter air takes its place next to the element and is cooled. The air cycles until the fridge is cool.

Convection currents also occur in nature:

- Land heats up from the Sun and heats the air above it. This air rises in currents called thermals.
- Gliders and birds use thermals to gain height.

Keeping Warm

Most houses waste energy. When the temperature is cold outside, energy is lost by heat escaping, mostly by convection.

The wasted heat can be reduced by insulating the house:

- Double glazing traps air between layers of glass.
- Curtains trap air.
- Loft insulation reduces the amount of hot air escaping through the roof.
- Cavity walls trap air. Cavities are often filled with insulation that reduces air movement.
- Draught proofing.
- Reflective foil on or in walls reduces heat loss by **radiation**.
- Insulation (lagging) around the hot-water tank.

In hot weather, a well-insulated house will also stay cooler by reducing the amount of heat coming into the house from outside.

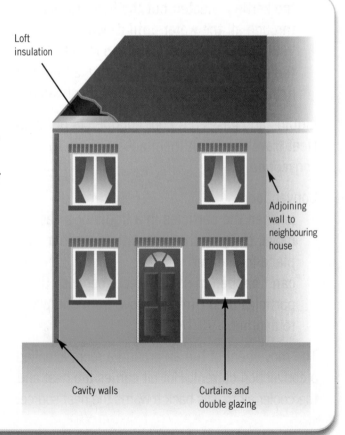

Loft insulation

Adjoining wall to neighbouring house

Cavity walls

Curtains and double glazing

Heat can travel when there are no particles to carry it. **Infrared** waves carry heat energy through air or through a vacuum. This is called radiation.

If you put your hand near something hot, you can feel the heat on your skin without touching it. The hotter the object, the more infrared energy it radiates. This is how the Sun's energy reaches the Earth.

Some infrared radiation can pass through glass:

* Infrared radiation from the Sun can pass through glass into a greenhouse because the Sun is very hot and it radiates high-energy radiation.
* The plants inside the greenhouse aren't so hot and radiate infrared radiation of lower energy that can't pass through the glass.
* The energy is trapped and the greenhouse heats up.

The Earth's atmosphere acts like the glass in a greenhouse, trapping energy from the Sun. Without this greenhouse effect, the Earth wouldn't be warm enough for life to exist.

However, polluting gases such as carbon dioxide (for example, from power stations) can increase the effect. This extra warming is known as **global warming** and could cause problems for humans, plants and animals.

Darker colours radiate more energy than lighter colours. Dark, dull surfaces also absorb more infrared energy than light, shiny surfaces.

Shiny surfaces reflect radiation. This is why on a sunny day it's a good idea to wear light colours to keep cool.

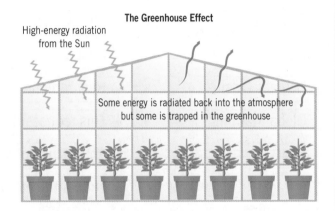

The Greenhouse Effect

High-energy radiation from the Sun

Some energy is radiated back into the atmosphere but some is trapped in the greenhouse

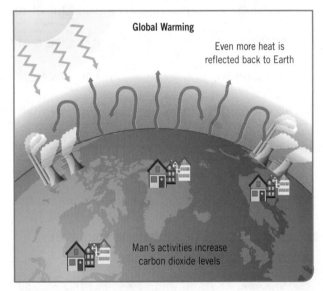

Global Warming

Even more heat is reflected back to Earth

Man's activities increase carbon dioxide levels

Quick Test

1. What unit is temperature measured in?
2. Which has more heat: a full bath at 25°C or a cup of tea at a temperature of 75°C?
3. In which direction does heat flow?
4. Name three ways in which heat travels.
5. What kind of waves carry heat energy?
6. Why is it better to wear light colours on a hot day?

KEY WORDS

Make sure you understand these words before moving on!

* Conduction
* Convection
* Degrees Celsius
* Global warming
* Heat
* Infrared
* Insulation
* Radiation
* Temperature
* Thermometer

Getting Hotter, Getting Colder

Key Words Exercise

Match each key word with its meaning.

Conduction	The way heat flows through a solid
Convection	A type of energy
Degrees Celsius	Heat radiation waves
Global warming	This reduces the amount of heat flow
Heat	An instrument used to measure temperature
Infrared	The Earth getting hotter as a result of the greenhouse effect
Insulation	The unit of temperature
Radiation	A measure of the hotness of a body
Temperature	The way heat travels through air or a vacuum
Thermometer	The way heat travels through gases or liquids

Comprehension

Read the passage about getting cold, then answer the following questions.

1. Where does the human body get the energy from to keep warm?

2. What percentage of energy is converted to heat when a muscle is moved?

3. At what temperature does the body stop working properly?

4. Describe two ways that heat loss can be reduced in a person suffering from hypothermia.

5. Describe two ways that the human body reacts when a person is suffering from hypothermia.

The human body keeps warm by transferring chemical energy in food to heat energy in the muscles. When a muscle moves, only about 15% of the energy used actually moves the muscle; the rest is converted to heat.

Mountain climbers keep warm because they're doing lots of exercise. Their hands and feet may get very cold but they can cope with the conditions, provided their body's core temperature doesn't drop below 37°C. If their core temperature drops below 35°C, their body stops working properly. This condition is known as hypothermia.

Lots of layers of clothing trap air and prevent heat loss by convection. A shiny blanket can be wrapped around someone with hypothermia to reflect the heat inwards and prevent heat loss by radiation.

A cold body will shiver to generate more heat in the muscles and the blood vessels will shrink so that heat isn't carried to the skin but is kept near important organs, such as the heart.

Testing Understanding

1 **Fill in the missing words to complete the sentences about heat on the move.**

a) Conduction is the method of heat flow in _____. When you stir soup

with a metal spoon, heat is _____ through the spoon and into your hand.

Metal is a _____ conductor.

b) If you stir the soup with a plastic or_____ spoon, the heat isn't transferred

through the spoon to your hand so quickly. These materials are known as _____.

c) In _____ and gases, heat travels by _____. Heat can't

travel by convection in a solid. In air and in a _____, heat can travel by

_____.

2 **Read the information below about the Thermos flask, then answer the questions that follow.**

The Thermos flask was invented by James Dewar about 100 years ago. It's usually used to keep drinks hot. Look at the diagram opposite of his first flask.

a) The vacuum prevents heat travelling in two ways. What are they?

b) What does the shiny silver surface do?

c) Fill in the missing words to complete the following sentence:

The stopper prevents evaporation and

hot air rising out of the flask. Hot air rising

is known as a _____

_____.

d) Modern flasks are very similar, but are often made of metal instead of glass because metal is stronger. What is the main disadvantage of using metal instead of glass?

e) Would a Thermos flask keep a cool drink cool? Explain your answer.

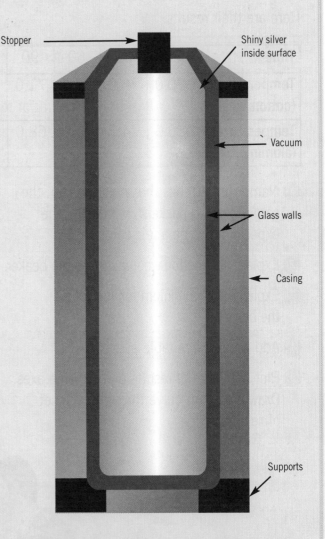

Stopper

Shiny silver inside surface

Vacuum

Glass walls

Casing

Supports

Getting Hotter, Getting Colder

Skills Practice

Richard and Sarah are investigating the cooling of hot water in beakers with different insulation.

Sarah insulates her beaker with layers of cotton wool. Richard insulates his beaker with layers of aluminium foil. They stir the water as it cools and take the temperature every 30 seconds.

Here are their results:

Time	0	30	60	90	120	150	180	210	240	270	300
Temperature (cotton wool)	80.0	76.0	73.5	71.0	69.0	67.5	66.0	65.0	64.5	64.0	63.5
Temperature (aluminium foil)	80.0	74.0	71.0	68.0	66.0	64.0	62.5	61.0	60.5	60.0	59.5

1. Name three things that must be kept the same for both beakers in order for the experiment to be a fair comparison.

2. Explain how cotton wool insulates the beaker.

3. Explain how aluminium foil insulates the beaker.

4. Add units to the table above.

5. Plot both sets of results on the same axes. Draw a smooth curve through each set of results.

6. Which material provides the best insulation?

7. Why do you think that some of the points don't lie exactly on the smooth curve? What could be done during the experiment to try to ensure that the line is smoother?

8. Sanjay did the same experiment, but his layers of aluminium foil weren't wrapped so tightly. There were air gaps in between the layers. Do you think this would make the foil a better or a poorer insulator? Explain your answer.

Responding to the Environment

Sensing and Doing

Every action you take is a **response** to a **stimulus**, for example...

- you prick your finger on a drawing pin (stimulus) and immediately pull your finger away (response)
- you put food into your mouth (stimulus) and produce saliva (response).

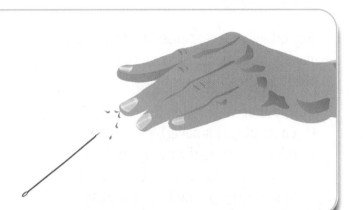

Nerve Impulses

Sensory nerves have **receptors** at one end that transform energy from one type to another. For example, chemical energy is transformed into electrochemical energy in the nerve cells.

An impulse then passes along to relay nerve cells (in the brain or spinal cord) and to **motor nerve** cells, which cause an action, like the movement of a muscle.

In this way, you respond to a variety of stimuli, (for example, smell, taste, movement, light, sound, heat and pressure, etc). The brain coordinates all these responses so that you show patterns of **behaviour**.

By learning, you can change your behaviour. For example, if you learn that a fire is hot then you try not to touch it. But very young babies don't know this, so a fire must be guarded to stop them touching it.

All living things have senses, for example...

- woodlice will move into dark, damp areas
- maggots will move away from light
- young seedlings will grow towards the light (even though plants don't have nerves).

Responding to the Environment

Moving

Very often, your response to a stimulus is to make a movement. To move your bones, you need muscles.

Muscles can...
- **contract** (get smaller)
- relax (return to their original state)
- only exert a force when contracting, which means they can pull but not push.

The muscles in your arm work in opposition to each other, so when one contracts, the other relaxes. This is an example of **antagonistic** action:
1. To move the forearm up, the biceps must contract and the triceps relaxes.
2. To move the forearm back again, the biceps must relax and the triceps contracts.

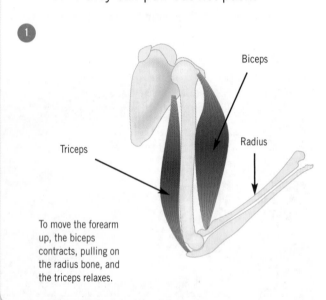

Biceps

Triceps

Radius

To move the forearm up, the biceps contracts, pulling on the radius bone, and the triceps relaxes.

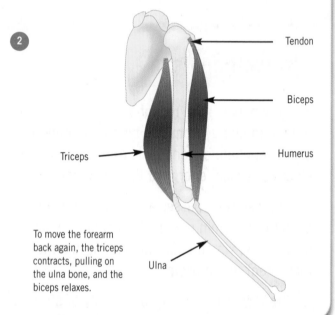

Tendon

Biceps

Triceps

Humerus

To move the forearm back again, the triceps contracts, pulling on the ulna bone, and the biceps relaxes.

Ulna

Joints

Bones don't bend, so in order for you to move easily they need joints. Some joints allow more movement than others, for example...
- the elbow and knee joints are hinge joints and only allow an up-and-down motion
- the shoulder and hip are ball-and-socket joints, which allow up, down and circular motion.

All joints need antagonistic pairs of muscles in order to work efficiently.

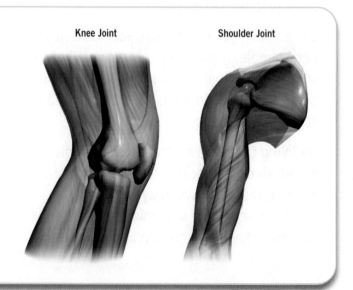

Knee Joint　　　　**Shoulder Joint**

Respiration

In order to move, muscles need energy. Energy is released during **respiration**.

Aerobic respiration is the process by which **oxygen** and **glucose** are combined to release energy for muscle and other cells to use. The equation is:

$$\text{glucose} + \text{oxygen} \longrightarrow \text{carbon dioxide} + \text{water} + \text{energy}$$

This is how aerobic respiration works:

- The glucose molecule contains a lot of energy. You get it from the digestion of carbohydrates.
- The oxygen is taken from the air in the lungs.
- Inside cells, the oxygen is combined with the glucose and this results in the glucose molecule being broken up. **Carbon dioxide** and water are waste products of this energy-releasing process.
- The more work a cell does, the more energy it needs, so when a muscle is working hard it needs more glucose and oxygen.
- This process also generates heat.

A Working Muscle Cell

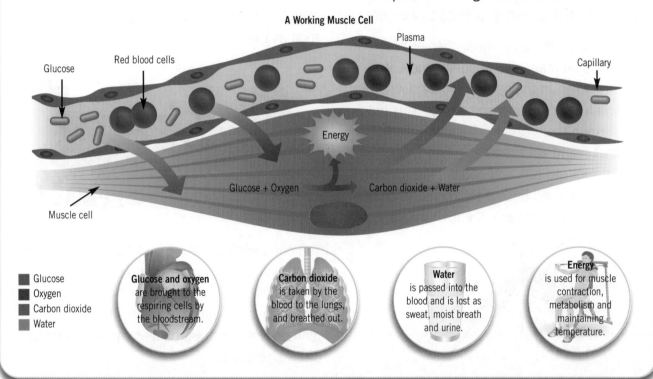

Plasma

Glucose

Red blood cells

Capillary

Energy

Glucose + Oxygen

Carbon dioxide + Water

Muscle cell

- Glucose
- Oxygen
- Carbon dioxide
- Water

Glucose and oxygen are brought to the respiring cells by the bloodstream.

Carbon dioxide is taken by the blood to the lungs, and breathed out.

Water is passed into the blood and is lost as sweat, moist breath and urine.

Energy is used for muscle contraction, metabolism and maintaining temperature.

Respiration Around the Body

Respiration is a process that goes on in every cell in the body to release energy from food.

The blood is very important because it carries oxygen from the lungs and glucose from the intestines to the cells for respiration.

Blood also carries away the carbon dioxide dissolved in the plasma (blood liquid) to the lungs. Water is taken to the kidneys so that it can be **excreted** (got rid of) from the body.

When you exercise, your heart and lungs have to work harder to get oxygen and glucose to the cells.

If the muscle cells don't get enough glucose or oxygen, they may become fatigued (tired) and stop working properly, which may result in cramp in the muscle. Cramp is where the muscle contracts and doesn't relax again, causing pain.

Responding to the Environment

Innate and Learned Behaviour

Behaviour in humans and animals is **either...**
- **innate** (instant and caused by genes) **or**
- **learned** (the result of experience).

The simplest type of innate behaviour is a reflex action like immediately pulling your hand away from a hot or sharp object. This behaviour protects you from harm. Some innate behaviour can be altered by experience.

These are examples of innate behaviour:
- Some animals, like woodlice, move very fast when in the open and only slow down when they're under something. This helps to keep them safe from animals or birds that might eat them.
- Mosquitoes bite and obtain food (blood) from exposed flesh if that person's body temperature attracts them.

Learned behaviour is developed through experience. Some animals start learning as soon as they're born and they will follow the first object they see that has certain characteristics.

For example, chicks will follow their mother and some geese will follow wellington boots worn by their owner if they see them first as soon as they hatch.

You can become used to a stimulus that offers no danger. For example, if you enter a room with a bad smell, at first you react. After a while, the smell 'goes' because the body realises that it's not a danger and so 'switches off' the response.

Quick Test

1. What is an action you take as a result of a stimulus called?
2. What is the term for a pattern of responses to a variety of stimuli?
3. When do muscles exert a force?
4. What do you call two muscles that work in opposition to each other?
5. Which gas does aerobic respiration use to help break down glucose?

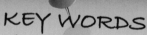

KEY WORDS

Make sure you understand these words before moving on!

- Antagonistic pair
- Behaviour
- Carbon dioxide
- Excretion
- Glucose
- Innate behaviour
- Learned behaviour
- Motor nerve
- Muscle contraction
- Oxygen
- Receptor
- Respiration
- Response
- Stimulus

Key Words Exercise

Match each key word with its meaning.

Key Word	Meaning
Antagonistic pair	Something that causes a response in the nerve cell
Behaviour	An action as a result of a nervous impulse, for example, moving a muscle
Carbon dioxide	A pattern of actions carried out by an animal
Excretion	The end of a sensory nerve that transforms one type of energy into a nerve impulse
Glucose	A type of nerve that causes an action to take place
Innate behaviour	When a muscle shortens to exert a force
Learned behaviour	Two muscles that work opposite to each other
Motor nerve	A combination of chemical reactions that release energy in a cell
Muscle contraction	Removal of waste products of chemical reactions from the body
Oxygen	The energy-rich molecule used in respiration
Receptor	A gas that's a waste product of respiration
Respiration	A gas used up to help break down glucose in respiration
Response	Behaviour that's instant and caused by genes
Stimulus	Behaviour that occurs as a result of experience

Comprehension

Read the passage about Ivan Pavlov, then answer the following questions.

1. Why did the dogs salivate when given food?

2. What were the two stimuli that were associated by the dogs?

3. Why did Pavlov have to use other dogs for this experiment?

4. How would this behaviour be of advantage to the dogs?

5. Describe a conditioned behaviour you might show.

In the late 1890s, a scientist called Ivan Pavlov noticed that the dogs he was studying would salivate when they knew they were about to be fed. He noticed that the dogs were able to recognise that food was on its way by a bell that rung every time the laboratory door was opened. So, he carried out a set of experiments on other dogs.

First he rang a bell, which caused no response in the dogs. Then, after the bell was rung, he gave the dogs food, which made them salivate. This was repeated several times.

Eventually, the dogs began to respond by salivating to the sound of the bell, even when no food was given. This is learning by association and is known as conditioned behaviour.

Responding to the Environment

1 **Fill in the missing words to complete the sentences about responding to the environment.**

a) Each action that a body makes is a _____ to a _____.

The pattern of actions shown is known as _____.

b) Sensory _____ have a _____ at one end that turns

one type of energy into a nerve / neurone _____.

c) When a muscle _____ it exerts a force but when it _____

it doesn't, so it can only _____ and not push. In order for a bone to

move one way, it needs one muscle, and to move the other way it needs a second. These

muscles are found in _____ pairs.

d) Energy from _____ is needed for a muscle to move. _____

helps to break down the energy-rich molecule _____ to release energy to

the muscle cell. If the muscle doesn't get enough energy then _____ sets

in and it can't work efficiently.

e) The behaviour shown as a result of all these actions is either caused by genes and is

_____ or is a result of experience, when it's _____.

It all adds up to make you unique in the way you behave.

2 **Study the diagram opposite showing a reflex pathway in a human, then answer the following questions.**

a) Label the receptor on the diagram.
b) Label the motor neurone and sensory neurone on the diagram.
c) Suggest a stimulus to the hand that might start a reflex response and describe the possible action.
d) Draw arrows on the diagram to show the direction of the path taken by the nervous impulses.

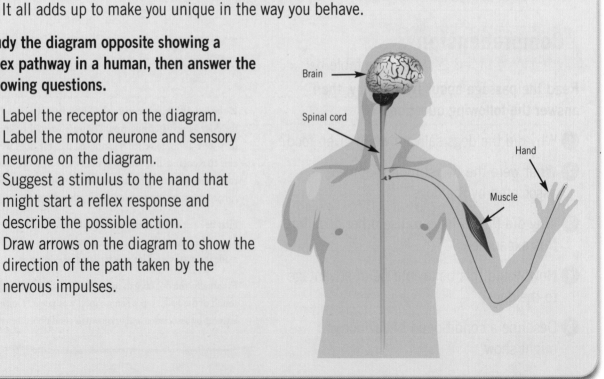

Brain

Spinal cord

Hand

Muscle

Terry and Trudi decided to find out the effect of temperature on the respiration rate of woodlice.

They set up the experiment as shown and carried it out in a range of temperatures. They took great care not to harm the animals as they did this.

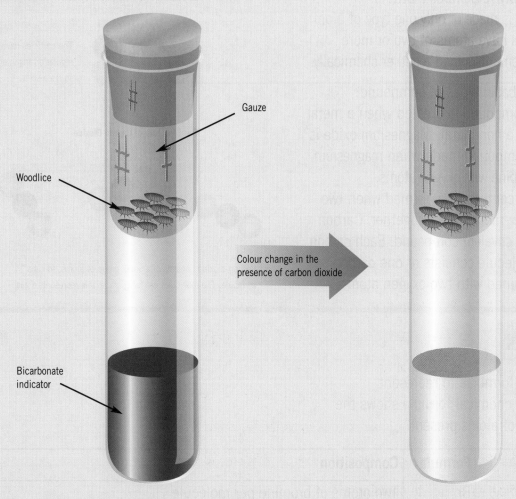

Gauze

Woodlice

Colour change in the presence of carbon dioxide

Bicarbonate indicator

They recorded their results in the table below.

Temperature (°C)	5	10	15	20	25	30	35	40
Time Taken to Turn Indicator Yellow (mins)	35	30	28	20	12	10	8	5

1. Plot the data onto a graph grid (label the axes clearly).

2. What conclusion can you draw from this graph?

3. Why do you think this pattern was shown?

4. Which is the independent variable (the variable that's being changed) in this investigation?

5. Why didn't Terry and Trudi increase the temperature higher than 40°C?

6. Which key variables would need to be carefully controlled in order to make this a fair test?

Compounds and Mixtures

How Atoms Combine to Form Compounds

You will probably remember that...
- an **element** is made of only one type of **atom**
- **compounds** have atoms of two or more different elements joined together chemically.

There are two basic types of compound:
- An ionic compound is created when a metal reacts with a non-metal. Magnesium oxide is an ionic compound made when magnesium atoms combine with oxygen atoms.
- A covalent compound is formed when two or more non-metals react together. Carbon dioxide is a covalent compound. Each carbon dioxide molecule consists of one carbon atom combined with two oxygen atoms.

The Structure of Magnesium Oxide

The particles have a regular arrangement, so it's a solid.

The Structure of Carbon Dioxide

Carbon dioxide consists of a small group of atoms, so it's a molecule. The molecules are far apart, so this represents a gas.

Formulae

Scientists use formulae to represent compounds. A chemical **formula** shows the type and ratio of atoms present.

Name	Formula	Composition
Bromine	Br_2	Two atoms of bromine per molecule
Sulfur dioxide	SO_2	One atom of sulfur and two atoms of oxygen per molecule
Copper carbonate	$CuCO_3$	One copper atom to one carbon atom to three oxygen atoms

Chemical Reactions

Compounds are new substances made by a **chemical reaction**. Here are two examples:

1 The non-metal hydrogen reacts with the non-metal oxygen to form the compound water.

Two molecules of hydrogen... $\rightarrow$ **$2H_2 + O_2$** $\rightarrow$ **$2H_2O$** ...to form two molecules of water
...react with one molecule of oxygen...

2 The metal sodium reacts with the non-metal chlorine to form the ionic compound sodium chloride.

Two sodium atoms... $\rightarrow$ **$2Na + Cl_2$** $\rightarrow$ **$2NaCl$** ...to form sodium chloride that has sodium and chlorine in the ratio 1:1.
...react with one chlorine molecule...

The Signs of a Chemical Reaction

Compounds can react chemically and when they do there are often 'tell-tale' signs that a chemical reaction has taken place.

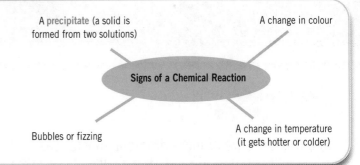

A precipitate (a solid is formed from two solutions)

A change in colour

Signs of a Chemical Reaction

Bubbles or fizzing

A change in temperature (it gets hotter or colder)

Chemical Reactions Involving Compounds

Here are some examples of chemical reactions involving compounds:

1 Sucrose is a type of sugar. When it's heated, a chemical reaction takes place:

sucrose ⟶ water vapour + carbon

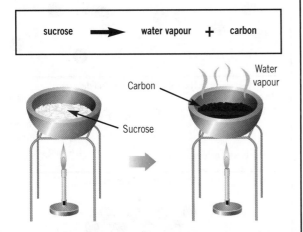

Water vapour

Carbon

Sucrose

2 When pieces of magnesium carbonate are added to a solution of hydrochloric acid, a chemical reaction takes place:

magnesium carbonate + hydrochloric acid ⟶ magnesium chloride + water + carbon dioxide

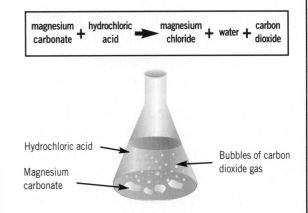

Hydrochloric acid

Magnesium carbonate

Bubbles of carbon dioxide gas

3 When a solution of iron chloride is added to a solution of sodium carbonate, a chemical reaction takes place:

sodium carbonate + iron chloride ⟶ sodium chloride + iron carbonate (precipitate)

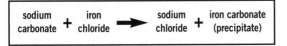

The iron carbonate is formed as a precipitate, an insoluble solid made when two solutions react together.

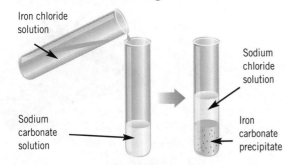

Iron chloride solution

Sodium carbonate solution

Sodium chloride solution

Iron carbonate precipitate

4 When a solution of ammonium hydroxide is added to a solution of copper sulfate, a chemical reaction takes place:

ammonium hydroxide + copper sulfate ⟶ ammonium sulfate + copper hydroxide (precipitate)

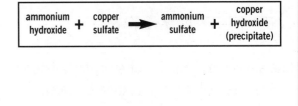

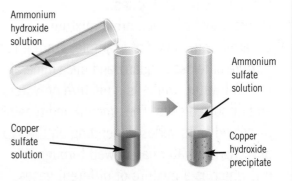

Ammonium hydroxide solution

Ammonium sulfate solution

Copper sulfate solution

Copper hydroxide precipitate

Compounds and Mixtures

Mixtures

In a **mixture**, two or more different substances are mixed together but not chemically joined.

Mixtures...
- don't have a fixed composition (i.e. they don't need to contain a fixed number of atoms and molecules)
- are easy to separate.

Compounds...
- do have a fixed composition
- are much harder to separate.

A mixture of iron and sulfur can be changed by adding more iron or more sulfur. The mixture can be separated by using a magnet. The magnet attracts the iron, which is **magnetic**.

If the mixture of iron and sulfur is heated gently, the iron atoms and the sulfur atoms become chemically joined. A new compound called iron sulfide (FeS) is formed. It has one iron atom for every sulfur atom. Iron sulfide has different properties from iron and sulfur. It's a black, non-magnetic powder.

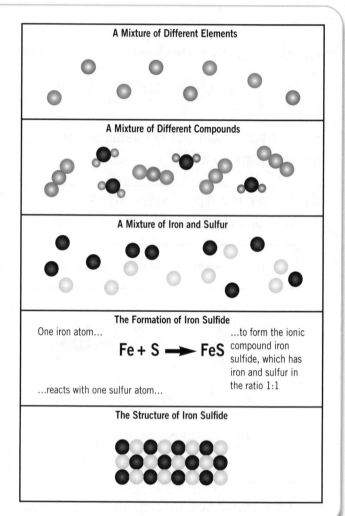

A Mixture of Different Elements

A Mixture of Different Compounds

A Mixture of Iron and Sulfur

The Formation of Iron Sulfide

One iron atom...

$$Fe + S \longrightarrow FeS$$

...to form the ionic compound iron sulfide, which has iron and sulfur in the ratio 1:1

...reacts with one sulfur atom...

The Structure of Iron Sulfide

Everyday Mixtures

Here are some examples of everyday mixtures:
- Seawater, which is a mixture of water, dissolved salts and gases.
- Rocks, most of which are a mixture of different minerals. For example, granite is a mixture of feldspar, quartz and mica minerals.
- Mineral water, which is a mixture of water and dissolved salts. The amount and type of dissolved salts varies depending on the type of rocks the water has flowed through.
- Air, which is a mixture of different gases.

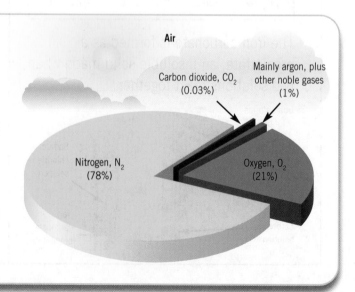

Air

Carbon dioxide, CO_2 (0.03%)

Mainly argon, plus other noble gases (1%)

Nitrogen, N_2 (78%)

Oxygen, O_2 (21%)

Fractional Distillation

Air can be separated by **fractional distillation**:
- First the air is cooled to -200°C. At this temperature, all the gases in air **condense** to form liquids.
- The liquid air is then placed in a fractional distillation column and is warmed up.
- As each liquid boils at a different temperature, the various gases can be collected and removed.

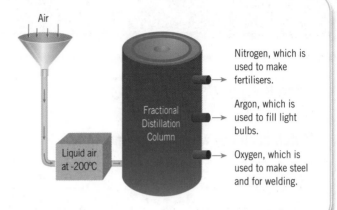

Melting and Boiling Points

When substances are heated or cooled they can change state, such as from solid to liquid or liquid to gas.

Pure elements and compounds melt and boil at fixed temperatures. Iron has a melting point of 1535°C and a boiling point of 2750°C. This means that...
- below 1535°C iron is a solid.
- between 1535°C and 2750°C iron is a liquid
- above 2750°C iron is a gas.

Because pure elements and compounds melt and boil at fixed temperatures, you can use melting points and boiling points to identify unknown substances.

Mixtures don't have fixed melting points and boiling points. Pure water boils at 100°C. If salt is added to pure water, a mixture is formed. The boiling point of the salty water is higher than pure water. The more salt that's added, the higher the boiling point becomes.

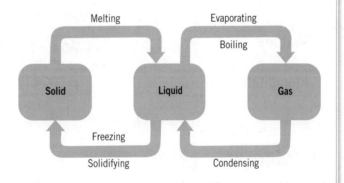

Quick Test

1. Name the compound formed when magnesium reacts with oxygen.
2. Name the compound formed when sodium reacts with chlorine.
3. A molecule of carbon dioxide has the formula CO_2. Explain what this formula means.
4. How can air be separated?

Compounds and Mixtures

Match each key word with its meaning.

Atom	A change in which new substances are made
Chemical reaction	A substance made of only one type of atom
Compound	A very small particle
Condense	Contains atoms of two or more different elements that are chemically joined
Element	A word describing a material that's attracted by a magnet
Formula	A way to separate mixtures of liquids that have different boiling points
Fractional distillation	Two or more different substances that are mixed together but not chemically joined
Magnetic	Turn from a gas to a liquid
Mixture	An insoluble solid made when two solutions react together
Precipitate	A code to represent the type and number of atoms present

Comprehension

Read the passage about nitrogen, then answer the following questions.

1. How is nitrogen obtained?

2. Describe an ammonia molecule.

3. What is a catalyst?

4. Why are fertilisers used?

5. Why is nitrogen needed by plants?

6. How can you tell that a plant doesn't have enough nitrogen?

Nitrogen is obtained by the fractional distillation of liquid air. Nitrogen is heated with hydrogen to produce the compound ammonia, NH_3. Each ammonia molecule contains one nitrogen atom and three hydrogen atoms. An iron catalyst is also used. A catalyst is a special chemical that increases the rate of reaction but isn't used up during the reaction. This means that a catalyst can be reused many times.

Ammonia is used to produce nitrogen fertilisers. Gardeners and farmers use fertilisers to help their plants grow better. Fertilisers help plants by replacing the nutrients that the plants use up as they grow. Nitrogen fertilisers are very important. Nitrogen makes plants grow better and produce lots of lush green leaves. If there isn't enough nitrogen, plants become stunted and start to turn yellow. This means that these plants will not produce high yields of crops.

1 **Fill in the missing words to complete the sentences about compounds and mixtures.**

a) _____, like copper, are made of only one type of atom. Compounds are made when _____ of two or more different elements are joined together by a chemical _____ .

b) The compound magnesium oxide is made when magnesium reacts with _____ . The compound carbon dioxide is made when _____ reacts with oxygen.

c) Compounds have a fixed _____ and are _____ to separate.

d) A _____ is formed when two or more substances are mixed together. Mineral water and most rocks are examples of everyday _____ .

e) Mixtures don't have a fixed _____ and are _____ to separate.

f) Air is a mixture. The main gases in air are _____ and oxygen. Air can be separated by the fractional _____ of liquid air.

2 **Study the diagrams, then answer the questions that follow.**

The symbols represent different types of atoms:

These diagrams show the arrangement of the atoms in four different substances:

| A | B | C | D |

a) Give the letter of the diagram that shows an element.
b) Give the letter of the diagram that shows one compound.
c) Give the letter of the diagram that shows a mixture of elements.
d) Give the letter of the diagram that shows a mixture of compounds.

Compounds and Mixtures

Skills Practice

Andy wants to find out if the amount of salt added to water affects its boiling point.

1 Pure water boils at 100°C. Draw an arrow on the temperature scale below to show the temperature at which pure water freezes.

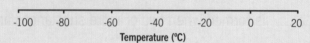

2 a) What piece of equipment should Andy use to measure the boiling point of the water?

b) What piece of apparatus should he use to measure the volume of water used in the experiment?

c) What piece of apparatus should he use to measure the amount of salt used in the experiment?

3 Complete the table below to show the different factors in Andy's experiment. Put one tick in each row.

	Factor to Change	Factor to Keep Same	Factor to be Measured
Temp. the Water Boils at			
Volume of Water			
Mass of Salt			

4 The table below shows the results from Andy's experiment.

Mass of Salt Added (g)	Boiling Temperature (°C)
0	100
0.5	102
1.0	102
1.5	103
2.0	104

a) Use this information to complete the graph.

b) Add a line of best fit.

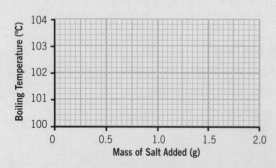

5 Andy decided to repeat the experiment. Suggest why this was a good idea.

Magnetism and Electromagnetism

Magnetism

These materials have magnetic properties, so they can be magnetised:

- Iron (a metal).
- Cobalt (a metal).
- Nickel (a metal).
- Steel (an alloy).

Even if these materials aren't magnetised, they're still **attracted** by other magnets.

Non-magnetic materials, such as plastic, wood and other metals, can't be magnetised and aren't attracted by magnets.

Magnetic Fields

The strongest forces from a magnet seem to come from the ends, the north-seeking pole (or north pole) and the south-seeking pole (or south pole) of the magnet.

The space around a magnet is called a **magnetic field**. You can study the field using iron filings:

- The magnetic **field lines** run from the north pole to the south pole.
- The magnetic field is strongest where the field lines are closest together.

The Earth has a magnetic field and pulls on the poles of a magnet. A compass is a tiny magnet that turns on a spindle. The north-seeking pole turns so that it points to the north pole. A bar magnet suspended from a string does the same.

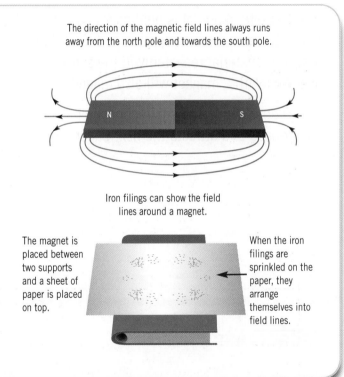

The direction of the magnetic field lines always runs away from the north pole and towards the south pole.

Iron filings can show the field lines around a magnet.

The magnet is placed between two supports and a sheet of paper is placed on top.

When the iron filings are sprinkled on the paper, they arrange themselves into field lines.

Attracting and Repelling

A magnet will always attract another magnetic material (e.g. an iron or steel bar) that isn't magnetised.

Two magnets will either attract or **repel** one another, depending on how they're arranged. Unlike poles attract but like poles repel.

Two like magnetic poles brought near to each other will repel each other.

Two unlike magnetic poles brought near to each other will attract each other.

Magnetism and Electromagnetism

Making a Magnet

A magnetic material...
- is full of tiny magnetic areas called **domains**.
- becomes magnetised when all the domains are lined up in the same direction.

Once a magnet is magnetised, it generally stays magnetised unless its magnetism is destroyed. Soft magnetic materials don't retain their magnetism because their particles rotate back to their random positions.

If a magnetic material is held near another magnet, it may become magnetised. Stroking a magnetic material repeatedly in the same direction with a magnet will also magnetise it.

Each paper clip in the chain opposite has been magnetised and attracts the next paper clip.

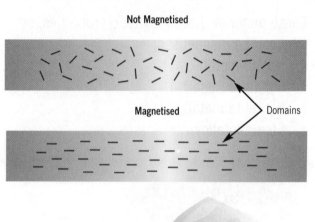

Not Magnetised

Magnetised — Domains

Electromagnets

A **coil** of wire will become magnetic when a direct current is passed through the coil. This is called an **electromagnet**.

Adding a **core** makes the electromagnet stronger. If the core is made of a soft magnetic material, such as iron, the magnet will 'switch off' when the current is turned off.

An electromagnet can also be made stronger by...
- increasing the number of turns of the coil
- increasing the current.

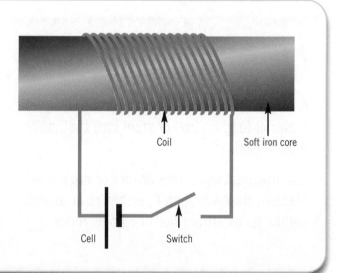

Coil

Soft iron core

Cell

Switch

Destroying a Magnet

A magnet becomes demagnetised when all the domains return to random positions. This can be done by...

- banging it with a hammer or dropping it
- heating it
- passing an alternating current through a coil of wire wrapped around the magnet.

Breaking a magnet in two doesn't destroy it; it simply creates two smaller magnets.

Uses of Magnets and Electromagnets

An electromagnet can do all the things that an ordinary magnet can, but it can also be switched on and off. The electromagnet opposite is being used to move a car in a scrap yard.

Electromagnets and magnets are used in many everyday devices including **circuit breakers**, electric bells, electric motors, loudspeakers, generators in power stations, credit cards and imaging scanners in hospitals.

A Maglev train is suspended above the rails by strong magnets, reducing friction.

The Circuit Breaker

A circuit breaker is a safety device that cuts off the current in a circuit if it gets too high:

- The current flows through the contact switch and the electromagnet.
- If the current gets too high, the pull of the electromagnet is strong enough to pull the soft iron bar to the right.
- The movement of the soft iron bar allows the reset button, attached to the contact switch, to spring upwards, breaking the circuit and stopping the current.
- Once the problem in the circuit has been fixed, pushing the reset button allows the current to flow again.

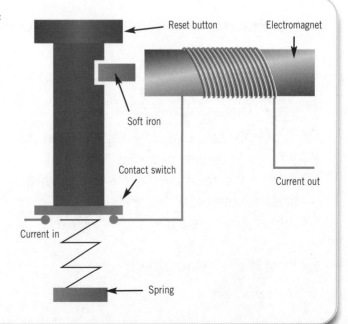

Magnetism and Electromagnetism

The Electric Bell

An electric bell works along the following principle:

- When the switch is closed, the electromagnet is switched on and attracts the soft iron.
- The movement of the soft iron pulls the hammer, which strikes the bell.
- When the hammer moves, the contacts are pulled apart, breaking the circuit.
- The current stops flowing and the electromagnet loses its magnetism.
- The contacts are pulled back together by the spring, switching the electromagnet back on.
- The repeated cycle of the hammer striking the bell causes the ringing of the bell.

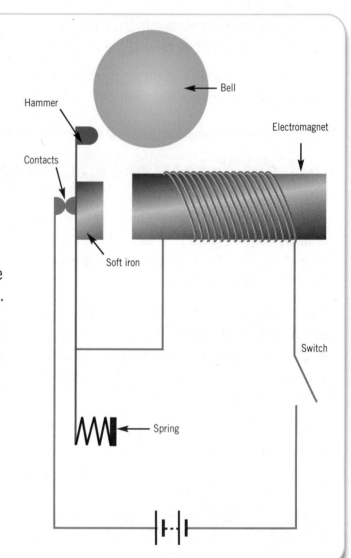

Quick Test

1. What is the space around a magnet known as?
2. What is a compass and what does it do?
3. What is the name given to the tiny magnetic areas in a magnetic material?
4. What happens to a magnet if it's broken in two?
5. What is an electromagnet?

Key Words Exercise

Match each key word to its meaning.

Key Word		Meaning
Attract		If a current is passed through this it becomes an electromagnet
Circuit breaker		A force that pulls together
Coil		The area around a magnet
Core		This will make an electromagnet stronger
Domains		A force that pushes away
Electromagnet		A safety device that switches off with high current
Field lines		Tiny magnetic areas inside some metals
Magnetic field		These show the strength and direction of a magnetic field
Repel		This can be magnetised but it doesn't retain its magnetism
Soft iron		A magnet that can be switched on and off

Comprehension

Read the passage about smashing particles, then answer the following questions.

1. What does a particle accelerator do?

2. Why do the particles need to be accelerated to such high speeds?

3. What is the purpose of the magnetic field in the Cyclotron?

4. What is the name of the largest and most powerful particle accelerator in the world?

A particle accelerator accelerates particles at very, very high speeds. The particles are smashed into other particles so that they break up. Particle accelerators are used to discover new particles and their behaviour.

The Cyclotron is a circular accelerator that consists of two metal half circles in between the north pole and the south pole of a huge magnet. The magnetic field accelerates the particles round and round until they're going fast enough for a collision.

The world's largest and most powerful particle accelerator is in Cern, an international physics laboratory in Switzerland. The powerful Large Hadron Collider uses a magnet that's as big as a house and as heavy as the Eiffel Tower!

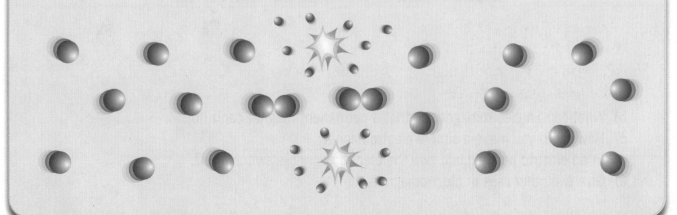

Magnetism and Electromagnetism

1. Use the following words to complete the sentences about magnetism and electromagnetism.

   attract   circuit   contact switch   current   electromagnet

   flow   high   reset   safety   spring

   a) A circuit breaker is a _____ device that uses an _____
   to switch off an electric current if it gets too _____.

   b) The current flows through a _____ and an
   electromagnet. If the _____ gets too high, the electromagnet becomes
   strong enough to _____ a soft iron bar. This allows the contact switch to
   _____ upwards, breaking the _____ and switching off
   the current.

   c) A circuit breaker can be _____ by pressing the reset button, allowing the
   current to _____ again.

2. Answer the questions below.

   a) Draw the shape of the field using field lines around the permanent magnet below.

   b) What can an electromagnet do that a permanent magnet can't do?
   c) How could you make a simple electromagnet?
   d) In an electric bell, explain how the electromagnet is switched off.
   e) Give two other uses of electromagnets.

Lorna and Douglas want to investigate how the strength of an electromagnet will increase when they increase the number of turns of the coil.

They plan to do this by counting the number of paper clips that can be suspended by the electromagnet. They have made a simple electromagnet by wrapping insulated wire around an iron nail.

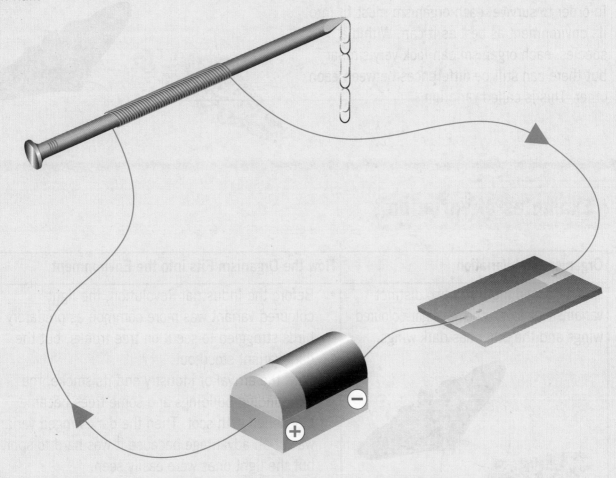

1 List the equipment that Lorna and Douglas will need to carry out the experiment.

2 Explain briefly how they should carry out the experiment.

3 The table below shows the results of their experiment. Plot the results on a graph and draw a curve through the points. Choose appropriate scales for your axes.

Number of Turns of the Coil	4	8	12	16	20	24
Number of Paper Clips Suspended	1	2	3	4	5	5

4 What is the relationship between the number of turns of the coil of the electromagnet and the number of paper clips that can be suspended?

5 Identify two sources of error in their experiment.

6 Suggest another way that they could make their electromagnet stronger.

Survival in the Environment

Fitting into the Environment

In order to survive, each organism must fit into its environment as best as it can. Within a species, each organism can look very similar but there can still be differences between each other. This is called **variation**.

Examples of Variation

Organism and Variation	How the Organism Fits into the Environment
The peppered moth has two distinct **variants** (versions): one has light-coloured wings and the other has dark wings.	• Before the Industrial Revolution, the light-coloured variant was more common as predatory birds struggled to see it on tree trunks, but the dark variant stood out. • With the arrival of industry and its smoke, the surrounding buildings and some trees became blackened with soot. Then the dark-winged variant was at an advantage because it was hard to spot, but the light ones were easily seen. • Both variants have advantages in different environments. They're still the same species and can interbreed easily, producing offspring of both variant types.
Some moles have larger feet than others.	In an environment where the soil is very hard, the large-footed moles are better able to dig through the soil to find food, like earthworms. In soft soils, neither variant is at any great advantage.
Different foxes have ears of a different size.	In a hot desert, foxes with larger ears find it easier to stay cool because their ears act as radiators, releasing excess heat. As a result, desert foxes with larger ears have an advantage over those with smaller ears.

Genes and Chromosomes

Variation is caused by organisms within a species having different genetic information in their cells:

- The **nucleus** of each cell contains thousands of **genes** arranged on threads called **chromosomes**, like links on a chain.
- The genes are the instructions that control all the **characteristics** organisms have.
- Even though organisms of the same species have a lot of genes in common, making them similar, the small differences create the variation between them.

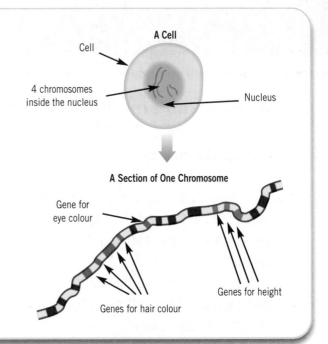

A Cell

Cell

4 chromosomes inside the nucleus

Nucleus

A Section of One Chromosome

Gene for eye colour

Genes for hair colour

Genes for height

Limitations of Variation

In most cases, the differences between organisms within a species are only small, so they don't really have an environmental advantage over each other.

For example, it's unlikely that the differences in the two cats opposite would make any difference to their ability to survive in any environment. Only large differences would create an advantage or disadvantage.

The differences in the genetic make-up of organisms are...

- entirely random and aren't a response to any change in the environment, so it's luck that produces an advantageous difference
- usually small, so it often takes a very long time (i.e. over many generations) for larger differences to develop and by then it may be too late for these changes to be an advantage
- sometimes a disadvantage rather than an advantage, as with the non-camouflaged bird opposite.

Usually, variation makes little difference to the survival of an organism; it simply makes the organism 'individual'.

Survival in the Environment

Genetic and Environmental Factors

Genetic variation can be passed on from one generation to the next, but differences caused by the environment can't be passed on:

- Sex, blood group and the shape of earlobes are genetic factors and aren't influenced by environmental factors.
- Strength, haircut and the ability to speak a language are the result of environmental and not genetic factors.
- Characteristics like height, personality, skin colour and hair colour can be the result of both environmental and genetic factors.

Identical twins have exactly the same genes because they were formed from the same fertilised egg, but their lifestyle and their experiences can affect them greatly.

Twins have the same genes but environmental factors can change their appearance.

Nature Versus Nurture

How much of the ability to play a sport well is down to genes and how much is down to practice and hard work? Can anyone be a great scientist or write a best-selling novel, or do you have to be born with the right genes?

You will have to try to decide because no-one really knows. This is the nature (genetic causes) versus nurture (environmental causes) debate.

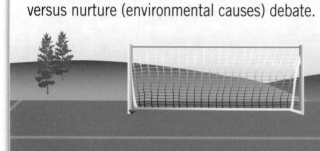

Examples of Survival

Characteristics **inherited** by one generation from another help organisms to survive in changing environments.

Although these genetic changes may be small, often the changes in the environment are also small. As a result, organisms showing variation survive:

Organism	How Genetic Variation Helps the Organism to Survive
Bluebell	Some bluebells grow earlier than others and are able to capture the light with little competition, allowing them to grow stronger and flower earlier.
Giraffe	A giraffe with a longer neck than others may be able to reach further up the trees to gain food, allowing it to survive better.
Olive tree	Olive trees traditionally like warm climates. But those that can withstand slightly cooler temperatures may be able to survive in Britain as climate change makes the conditions more favourable for them.
Staphylococcus bacteria	Those Staphylococcus bacteria that have **resistance** to **antibiotics** (drugs that have come from microbes) have caused problems in hospitals, for example **MRSA** (methicillin-resistant Staphylococcus aureus) infections. This is because they've been able to survive antibiotic treatment.
Rat	Some rats can survive even when the poison Warfarin has been laid to try to kill them. As a result, other types of poison have to be used.

Quick Test

1. What name is given to the differences in characteristics among organisms of the same species?
2. What is the cause of the differences between these organisms?
3. What is the name of the thread-like structures found in a nucleus?
4. Apart from inherited characteristics, what other factors may affect how a person looks?

KEY WORDS
Make sure you understand these words before moving on!
- Antibiotics
- Characteristics
- Chromosome
- Environmental factors
- Genes
- Genetic factors
- Inheritance
- MRSA
- Nucleus
- Resistance
- Variant
- Variation

Survival in the Environment

Key Words Exercise

Match each key word with its meaning.

Antibiotics	Differences within a single species
Characteristics	An organism that shows a certain difference in a species
Chromosome	The part of the cell where the genetic material is found
Environmental factors	Units that determine an organism's characteristics
Genes	Those features that can be seen in or on an organism
Genetic factors	A disease often found in hospitals, caused by a bacterium
Inheritance	Features of the surroundings that may affect an organism
MRSA	Influences on the genetic material of an organism
Nucleus	The passing on of characteristics from one generation to the next
Resistance	Drugs, produced from microbes, that are used to control bacterial infections
Variant	The ability to be relatively unaffected by something, for example, a drug
Variation	A thread-like structure, like a string of beads

Comprehension

Read this description of David, then answer the following questions.

1. Which of David's features do you think are inherited?

2. Which features do you think are affected by the environment?

3. Which features may be a result of both the environment and genes?

David has brown hair, in which he has dyed blond highlights, and green eyes. He is quite tall and quite skinny, but he can run fast and is the star member of the local basketball team. He recently went on a basketball tour in southern Italy and his skin has turned quite pink as a result.

His eyebrow is pierced and he has a scar on his right knee where he fell off his bike when he was very young. He has a straight nose and large ears that stick out.

Testing Understanding

1 **Fill in the missing words to complete the sentences about survival in the environment.**

a) Variation is differences in _____ between individuals.

b) Characteristics may be passed on from parents to their offspring in their
_____. These are _____ factors.

c) Characteristics that are affected by our surroundings are _____ factors.

d) Differences between individuals of the same _____ may allow them to
_____ in an environment that's changing.

e) Some features are a result of both types of factor and many people are unsure of just how
much of each type is really responsible. This argument is called the _____
versus _____ debate.

2 **Study the boxes below about why dinosaurs became extinct millions of years ago, then answer the questions that follow.**

Here is some information about dinosaurs and plants:	Here are some ideas about why the dinosaurs became extinct:
• Most dinosaurs ate plants. • Most dinosaurs were the largest animals alive at that time. • Plants can't grow without the Sun. • Dinosaurs couldn't survive very cold conditions.	• A new disease killed them. • A new predator killed them. • New animals ate all their food. • A huge meteorite hit the Earth, resulting in dust blocking out the Sun.

a) Using this information, choose an idea that you think isn't very likely to have happened.
Give a reason for your answer.

b) Explain how a meteorite could have been the cause of the dinosaurs' extinction.

Survival in the Environment

Fiona and Nigel carried out an experiment to see if the camouflage of an insect helped to prevent it from being eaten by birds.

To do this, they made 'insects' from bread and used food colourings to dye them different colours.

Then they placed equal numbers of coloured 'insects' on different pieces of coloured card and placed them randomly in the school garden.

They hid and watched the garden for two hours, then counted the 'insects' left.

Their results are shown in the table below.

1. What conclusions can you make from these results? Give reasons for your answer.

2. Why did Fiona and Nigel have to watch the garden during the investigation?

3. How could they improve this investigation?

4. What factors did they need to try to control in this investigation?

Colour of 'Insect'	Colour of Card	Number of 'Insects' at Start	Number of 'Insects' After Two Hours
Red	Red	10	8
Yellow	Yellow	10	7
Blue	Blue	10	6
Red	Yellow	10	1
Yellow	Blue	10	6
Blue	Red	10	2
Red	Blue	10	0
Yellow	Red	10	6
Blue	Yellow	10	2

What Rocks are Made of

Most rocks are mixtures of different minerals, naturally-occurring solid compounds with a crystalline structure. There are three types of rock:

Rock Type	Properties	Examples	
Sedimentary	These rocks are made of grains that are stuck together. They're formed in layers when sediment is deposited. They're quite soft and crumbly.	Sandstone	Limestone
Metamorphic	These rocks are made of interlocking crystals. They're formed when existing rocks are changed by high temperatures and pressures. They're hard, smooth and shiny, and may have layers of crystals.	Slate	Marble
Igneous	These rocks are made of interlocking crystals. They're formed when molten (liquefied) rock cools down and solidifies. The size of the crystals depends on the rate of cooling. These rocks are very hard.	Basalt	Granite

Porous and Non-Porous Rocks

In sedimentary rocks, the shape of the grains means that they can't interlock and there are gaps between them. These rocks are porous – there are gaps for air or water to get into.

In metamorphic and igneous rocks, the mineral crystals interlock with no holes or gaps between them. These rocks are non-porous – there are no gaps for air or water to get into.

If a porous rock is placed in water:
- Bubbles appear as air is lost from the rock.
- The mass of the rock increases as the gaps between the grains become filled with water.

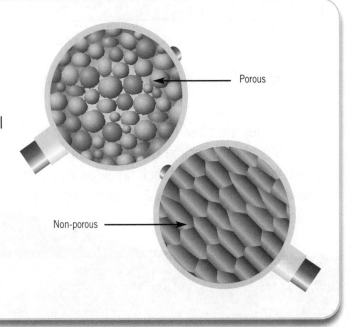

Porous

Non-porous

Rocks and Weathering

Physical Weathering

Temperature changes can break down rocks in two ways:

Type of Weathering	Description
Freeze-thaw Weathering 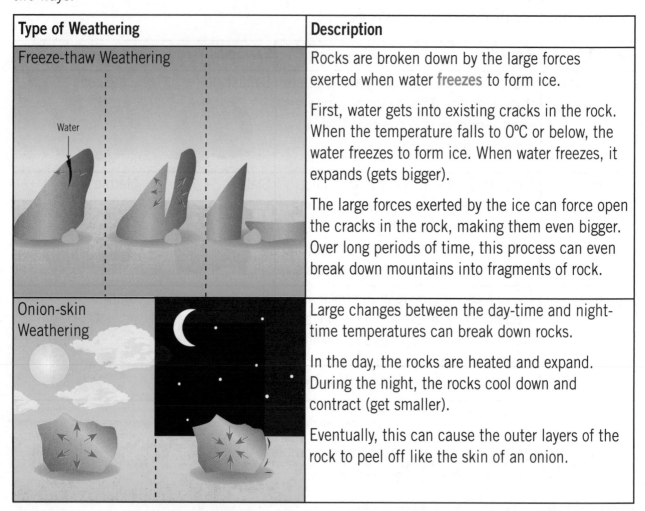	Rocks are broken down by the large forces exerted when water **freezes** to form ice. First, water gets into existing cracks in the rock. When the temperature falls to 0°C or below, the water freezes to form ice. When water freezes, it expands (gets bigger). The large forces exerted by the ice can force open the cracks in the rock, making them even bigger. Over long periods of time, this process can even break down mountains into fragments of rock.
Onion-skin Weathering	Large changes between the day-time and night-time temperatures can break down rocks. In the day, the rocks are heated and expand. During the night, the rocks cool down and contract (get smaller). Eventually, this can cause the outer layers of the rock to peel off like the skin of an onion.

Landscapes and Weathering

Scree slopes are often found at the bottom of rock cliffs. As the rock in the cliff face is weathered, fragments of rock break away. These fragments fall down and form a smooth scree slope.

How Rainwater Causes Rocks to Weather

Air contains small amounts of carbon dioxide. Carbon dioxide dissolves in rainwater to form carbonic acid, so rainwater is naturally slightly acidic. This acidic rain can cause the chemical weathering of rocks.

In polluted areas, gases, including sulfur dioxide from industrial processes and nitrogen oxides from car exhausts, may also dissolve in rainwater.

Sulfur dioxide and nitrogen oxides lower the pH of the rainwater even more to form acid rain. This speeds up the chemical weathering.

If the rainwater falls on rocks that contain metal carbonates, such as limestone, the rocks are weathered more quickly. When rocks are weathered, they become discoloured. Weathering can damage the detail on statues.

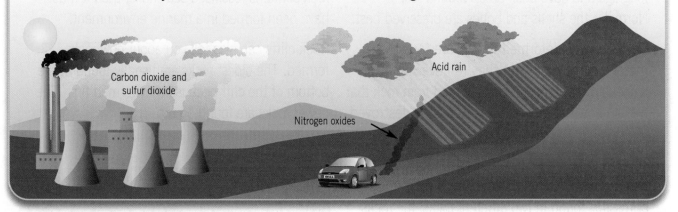

Carbon dioxide and sulfur dioxide

Nitrogen oxides

Acid rain

Transportation

Pieces of rock can be transported by glaciers, wind or rivers:

- Glaciers are slow-moving rivers of ice that can carry pieces of rock. When the glaciers melt, the fragments are deposited.
- When rocks are weathered, only the hardest materials (e.g. sand grains) remain. The wind can blow sand grains great distances. As the sand grains travel, they rub against each other and become more rounded.
- Rivers carry smaller fragments of rock further than larger pieces. As the pieces move, they rub against each other and against the river bed, making them smaller and more rounded. When the river can no longer carry the particles, they're deposited as layers of sediment. Grains of a similar size are deposited at the same time.

Where a River Deposits Rock Fragments

Large grains deposited here

Medium grains deposited here

Small grains deposited here

Rock fragments become more rounded as they move down the river bed.

Evaporates

Layers of sediment can also be formed when water that contains dissolved salts evaporates.

The salts are left behind as layers of solid sediment. These minerals are called evaporates.

Rocks and Weathering

Fossils and Evidence About the Past

Some sedimentary rocks contain **fossils**. Fossils are the remains of plants and animals that lived long ago and have been preserved in rock. Normally, the shells and bones are preserved best.

Occasionally, deformed fossils are found in metamorphic rocks but they're never found in igneous rocks. Igneous rocks formed from rock that was so hot that any remains would be destroyed.

Fossils form when dead plants and animals are covered in sediment before they can rot away. You can use fossils to help date rocks. If the same type of fossil is found in two different rocks, the rocks were formed at the same time.

Fossils can also tell you about the conditions that existed when the rocks formed. For example, if a rock contains fossilised sea shells, then it must have been formed in a marine environment.

Rock cliffs can also tell you about how rocks formed. The oldest rocks are usually found at the bottom of the cliff because they formed first. The newer rocks are found on top.

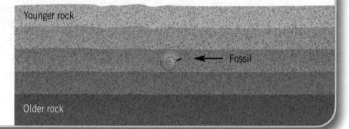

Fossil Fuels

Coal, oil and natural gas are **fossil fuels**. Coal is formed from the remains of dead plants, and oil and natural gas are formed from the remains of dead sea creatures and plants.

Fossil fuels are non-renewable – they take millions of years to form, which is much slower than the rate they're being used up.

Fossil fuels contain carbon. When they're burned, carbon dioxide is formed and this gas contributes to global warming:

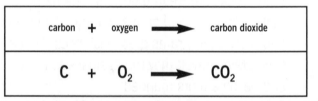

carbon + oxygen ⟶ carbon dioxide

$$C + O_2 \longrightarrow CO_2$$

Quick Test

1. Which types of rock contain interlocking crystals?
2. What happens when a porous rock is placed in water?
3. How can ice weather rock?
4. How is acid rain formed?
5. What is a glacier?
6. What happens to rocks as they're carried by a river?

KEY WORDS
Make sure you understand these words before moving on!
- Deposit
- Evaporates
- Fossil fuels
- Fossils
- Freeze
- Glacier
- Interlocking
- Mineral
- Porous
- Sediment

Key Words Exercise

Match each key word with its meaning.

Key word	Meaning
Deposit	The remains of dead plants and animals
Evaporates	Solids that are deposited by a river
Fossil fuels	Lay down
Fossils	A slow-moving river of ice
Freeze	Turn from liquid to solid
Glacier	Joined together with no gaps
Interlocking	A naturally-occurring solid compound with a crystalline structure
Mineral	Minerals formed when water that contains dissolved salts evaporates
Porous	Energy resources including coal, oil and natural gas
Sediment	Contains gaps between grains that air or water can enter

Comprehension

Read the passage about the great fossil finder, Mary Anning, then answer the following questions.

1. Where was Mary Anning born?

2. Why did Mary and her brother start to collect fossils?

3. Why was fossil collecting a dangerous thing to do?

4. Describe an ichthyosaur.

5. Name Mary's other outstanding fossil finds.

6. How did Mary's findings show that species could become extinct?

Mary Anning was born in 1799 in the town of Lyme Regis, Dorset, on the south coast of England. From an early age Mary seemed marked out for a remarkable life. When she was a baby, she was one of four people struck by a lightning bolt. Mary was the only one to survive.

When Mary's father died of tuberculosis, Mary and her brother Joseph collected fossils from the cliffs near Lyme Regis, which they sold to earn money for the family. This was very dangerous because the cliffs were unstable. High tides and storms dislodged pieces of rock and exposed fossils, but the cliffs could easily collapse and bury the children.

A few months after her father's death, 12-year-old Mary discovered the first complete fossilised skeleton of a crocodile-like dinosaur called an ichthyosaur. She later discovered the first examples of a plesiosaur and a pterosaur.

She became known as the 'greatest fossil finder the world has ever known', even though society and science were dominated by men at the time.

Mary's discoveries were important because they provided evidence of animals that had existed in the past but weren't alive today, so they showed that species could become extinct. She gave an insight to our understanding of who we are and our place in the universe. The tongue twister 'she sells sea-shells on the sea shore' keeps her memory alive.

Rocks and Weathering

Testing Understanding

1 **Fill in the missing words to complete the sentences about rocks and weathering.**

a) Most _____ are mixtures of different minerals. Sandstone and limestone are

_____ rocks. They're made of grains that are stuck _____.

b) Marble and slate are _____ rocks. Granite and basalt are _____

rocks. Both of these types of rock have interlocking _____. There are no

_____ between the crystals so these rocks aren't porous.

c) Water can weather rocks. Water gets into existing _____ and when it freezes it

changes state from liquid to _____. As the ice forms, it _____

and pressure builds up on the cracks, causing them to be pushed _____

apart. Temperature changes can also cause _____-skin weathering.

d) Normal rainwater is slightly acidic because it contains trace amounts of the gas, carbon

_____. This _____ the pH of the rainwater. Rainwater

weathers all rocks but rocks containing metal _____ weather faster.

e) In polluted areas, sulfur dioxide can dissolve in rainwater to form _____ rain.

This reduces the _____ of the acid even more and speeds up the rate of

chemical weathering.

2 **Study the diagram opposite of a cliff face, then answer the questions.**

a) Which is the oldest type of rock?
Explain your answer.

b) The limestone contains a fossil of a seashell. What is a fossil?

c) What does this fossil tell you about the conditions in which this limestone was formed?

d) An identical fossil was found in another type of rock further down the coast. What does this tell you about these two rocks?

e) Explain how ice can cause the weathering of the rocks in this cliff face.

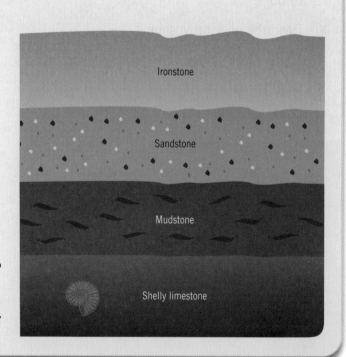

Ironstone

Sandstone

Mudstone

Shelly limestone

Ed uses a pH meter to measure the pH of four water samples.

The table below shows his results.

Water Sample	pH of the Solution
A	7.0
B	5.2
C	6.4
D	4.8

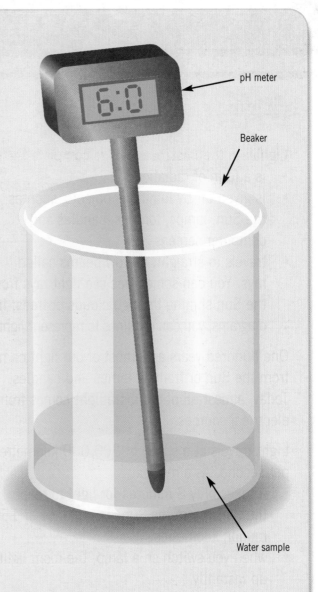

pH meter

Beaker

Water sample

1 Complete the bar chart below to show the pH of each water sample.

2 Suggest an advantage of using a pH meter rather than universal indicator paper to measure the pH of the water samples.

3 Water sample C is slightly acidic because carbon dioxide has dissolved in the rainwater. Carbon dioxide is formed when carbon is burned in oxygen. Complete the word equation below to sum up this reaction.

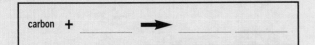

carbon + ... ➡ ....

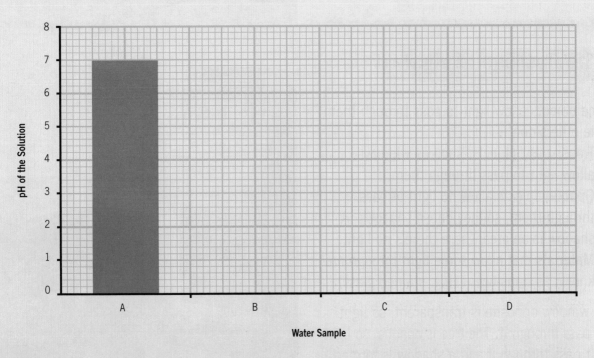

pH of the Solution

Water Sample

Light Rays

Light

Light...
- is a form of radiation
- is given off by **luminous** objects, such as the Sun, lamps, torches, candles and computer screens
- travels in straight, narrow beams called rays. You can sometimes see light rays from the Sun shining through clouds or trees. In diagrams, you can use lines to represent light.

One hundred years ago, most of our light came from the Sun or from oil lamps and candles. Today, almost all of our extra light comes from electrical sources.

Light travels at a speed of 300 000 kilometres per second. As a result...
- it takes only 8 minutes for light to reach the Earth from the Sun – a distance of 150 million kilometres
- when you switch on a lamp, the room lights up instantly.

The Passage of Light

Some objects allow light to pass through them while others don't:
- **Transparent** objects, such as windows, allow light to pass through them.
- **Opaque** objects allow no light to pass through them, so they cause **shadows**. A shadow is an area where there's no light.
- Materials that allow some light through are known as **translucent** (e.g. stained glass).

The window opposite is transparent, so light can pass through it. The tree is opaque, so light can't pass through it and a shadow is formed.

How You See Things

Most objects that you see don't give off their own light. You see them because light rays from luminous objects bounce off them into your eyes. This is called **reflection**.

An object in a dark room can't be seen until the lamp is switched on. Then light shines onto the object from the lamp and reflects into your eyes. The Moon reflects light from the Sun, enabling you to see it at night, even when you can't see the Sun.

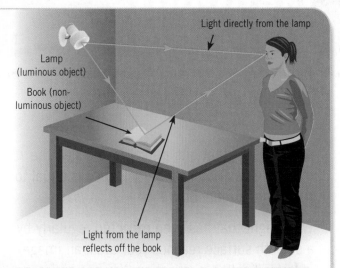

Light directly from the lamp

Lamp (luminous object)

Book (non-luminous object)

Light from the lamp reflects off the book

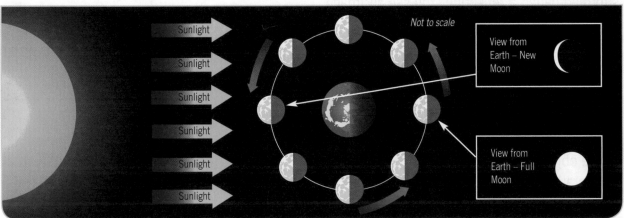

Sunlight

Not to scale

View from Earth – New Moon

View from Earth – Full Moon

Reflection

When light rays hit a surface, they're...
- reflected
- absorbed **or**
- transmitted through the material.

A rough surface (e.g. paper or wood) **scatters** the light so that it reflects in all directions.

Smooth surfaces (e.g. glass, mirrors and polished metal) reflect the light in a regular way so an image, or a reflection, can be seen.

Uneven surface – the light is scattered.

Even surface – the light is reflected regularly.

Light Rays

Reflection and Images

A ray of light that hits a surface is called the **incident ray**. The angle of incidence is equal to the angle of reflection.

When light that has been reflected regularly by a smooth surface reaches your eyes, an image is formed called a reflection. You see an image because your brain doesn't see the light bend at the surface; it sees the light rays as if they're coming from inside the mirror.

A reflection is...
- the same size as the object
- the same distance from the mirror as the object
- laterally inverted (left becomes right and right becomes left)
- a **virtual** image (it can't be focussed on a screen; you can only see it by looking into the mirror).

Mirrors can help drivers to see around corners. They can also be used to make a periscope, to see around corners or over crowds.

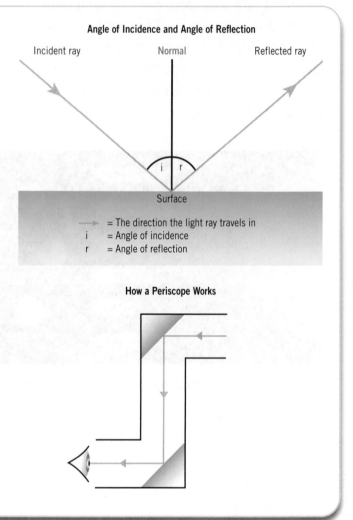

Angle of Incidence and Angle of Reflection

Incident ray   Normal   Reflected ray

Surface

→ = The direction the light ray travels in
i = Angle of incidence
r = Angle of reflection

How a Periscope Works

Refraction – Bending Light Rays

When light travels through transparent materials, such as water or glass, it travels slower than it travels in air or in a vacuum.

As a result...
- when light enters water or glass it bends (**refracts**) towards the normal
- when light leaves water or glass it speeds up and refracts away from the normal.

Because of refraction, water looks shallower than it really is and a pen standing in a glass of water looks like it bends at the surface.

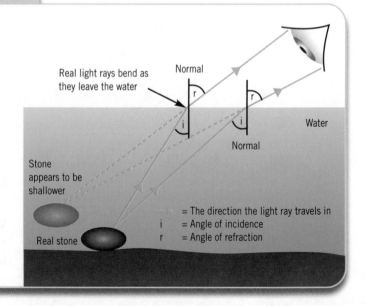

Real light rays bend as they leave the water

Normal

Water

Normal

Stone appears to be shallower

Real stone

→ = The direction the light ray travels in
i = Angle of incidence
r = Angle of refraction

Colour

When white light passes through a triangular prism made of glass or plastic, a spectrum is formed of all its constituent colours. Light behaves as if it travels in waves. White light contains light of different wavelengths and each wavelength is seen by your eyes as a different colour.

When the light passes through the prism, the different wavelengths are spread out and a spectrum is formed. This is because the light is refracted by the prism. The angle of refraction is different for each wavelength, so the different colours are seen. In the same way, a rainbow is formed by sunlight shining through droplets of rain.

Lighter coloured objects reflect more light than darker objects:

- White objects reflect all the light that hits them.
- Black objects absorb all the light that hits them.
- A red object absorbs light of all wavelengths except the wavelength that you see as red light, which is reflected.
- A blue object absorbs light of all wavelengths except the wavelength that you see as blue light, which is reflected.

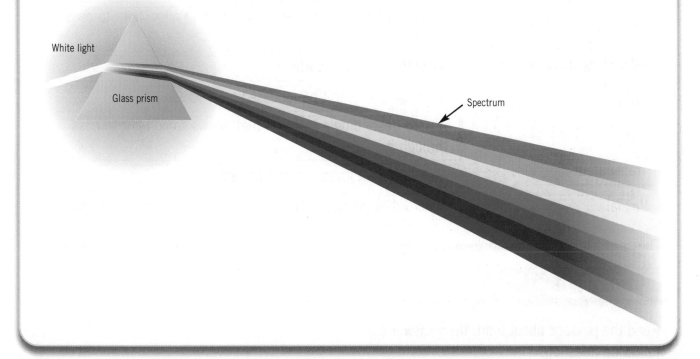

White light

Glass prism

Spectrum

Quick Test

1. What is a luminous object?
2. How long does it take light to reach the Earth from the Sun?
3. If light hits a rough surface, what happens to it?
4. Give two properties of a reflection in a mirror.
5. Why does water look shallower than it actually is?

Light Rays

Key Words Exercise

Match each key word with its meaning.

Key word	Meaning
Incident ray	The bending of light when it changes speed
Luminous	Light reflected in all directions
Normal	A line drawn at right angles to a surface at the point where the incident ray hits the surface
Opaque	Light rays that bounce off a surface
Reflection	An area where there's no light
Refraction	A word describing a material that doesn't allow light to pass through it
Scattering	A ray that strikes a surface
Shadow	An image that can't be focussed on a screen
Translucent	A word describing a material that allows some light to pass through it
Transparent	An object that gives out its own light
Virtual	A word describing a material that allows light to pass through it

Comprehension

Read the passage about light, then answer the following questions.

1. In the 1600s, why did most scientists prefer Newton's theory of light?

2. In the 1800s, Huygens's theory became more popular. Explain why.

3. How did Einstein change this belief in the early 1900s?

4. What is wave-particle duality?

In the 1600s, Christian Huygens, a Dutch physicist, claimed that light behaved as a wave, in a similar way to water or sound waves, travelling in straight lines. At about the same time, Isaac Newton put forward a theory that light travelled as tiny particles that moved through the air. Most scientists preferred Newton's ideas because he used his ideas to explain reflection and refraction, and he was well known for other impressive scientific ideas.

In the early 1800s, other scientists showed behaviour of light that could only be explained with wave ideas. Huygens's theory became more popular. However, in the early 1900s, Albert Einstein proved that light behaved as a particle, using evidence from an experiment carried out by Max Planck, a German physicist.

Today it's accepted that light can be thought of as two different things, a wave and a particle. Some of light's behaviour can be described with waves, and some with particles. This theory is known as wave-particle duality.

Testing Understanding

1 **Fill in the missing words to complete the sentences about light rays.**

    a) Objects that give off their own light are known as _____ objects. You see

        other objects because light from luminous sources _____ off them into

        your _____.

    b) _____ materials allow light to pass through them,

        _____ materials don't allow any light to pass through them and

        _____ materials allow some light to pass through them.

    c) Light travels in _____ lines. This means that an opaque object creates an

        area where there's _____ light, called a _____.

2 **Answer the questions about reflection.**

The diagram below shows a ray of
light striking a flat mirror.

    a) Draw a normal at the point where
        the ray hits the mirror.
    b) Label the angle of incidence.
    c) Complete the ray to show the path
        of the reflected ray.
    d) Label the angle of reflection.

Light Rays

Amy and Syama design an experiment to investigate how the angle of refraction changes for different materials. They have two blocks of different materials (glass and Perspex), some paper, a pencil, a ruler and a ray box.

1 Name a suitable instrument that can be used to measure the angles.

2 Syama suggests that they should repeat the experiment three times for each material. Suggest why this is a good idea.

3 Draw a diagram of a ray of light entering a block of glass. Label the normal, the incident ray, the refracted ray, the angle of incidence and the angle of refraction.

4 Amy suggests that they should repeat the experiment to find the angle of refraction when a ray of light enters a beaker of water. Give two reasons why the angle of refraction they measure will probably not be exactly the same as the true angle of refraction for water.

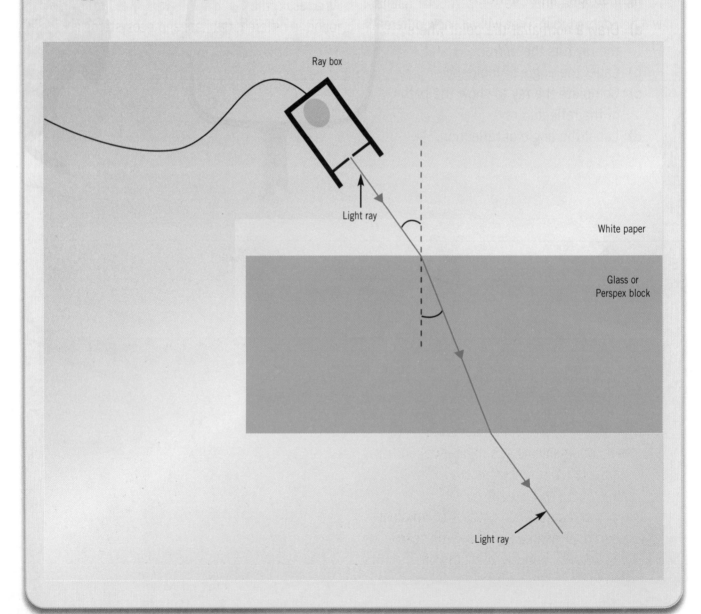

Ray box

Light ray

White paper

Glass or Perspex block

Light ray

Environmental Relationships

Describing an Environment

These terms help you to describe an environment:

- **Habitat** – the particular type of area in which an organism lives.
- **Population** – the total number of individuals of the same species that live in a habitat.
- **Community** – all the different organisms living in a habitat (the total of all populations).
- **Ecosystem** – the total community of living things, together with all the physical features (rainfall, temperature, wind, water, light, etc) in the habitat.

Types of Interaction Within Environments

All the organisms that live in a particular habitat will be adapted to it. They will all show different characteristics that help them to survive and breed to maintain the population size.

As a result, the **biodiversity** (variety of life) found in different habitats and ecosystems is very different.

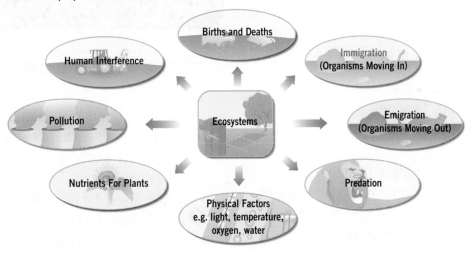

Size of Populations

The **distribution** (spread) and abundance (numbers) of organisms in a habitat depend on...

- the adaptation of the organism to the surrounding environment
- how much competition there is (from other species and members of the same species)
- the number of births and deaths (from predation, disease, etc).

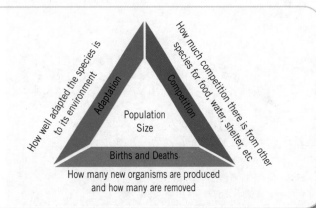

Environmental Relationships

Collecting Habitat Data

The best way to collect the correct data is to count everything and measure everything. But this is never really practical, so you have to sample a habitat and use the sample to estimate the totals.

Estimating Populations

Once the animals have been trapped and counted, they can be marked in some way, for example, with a spot of paint. The organisms can then be released.

After a time, another sample can be trapped and a mathematical formula used to estimate the population size. This is called a 'capture-recapture' technique.

For plants and some very slow animals, you can use quadrats. Quadrats are usually squares (but they can be any shape) of a known area:
- They're randomly placed in the habitat.
- The numbers of organisms found in each quadrat are counted and the total data is used to estimate the population.

Remember not to harm any organisms and return everything afterwards.

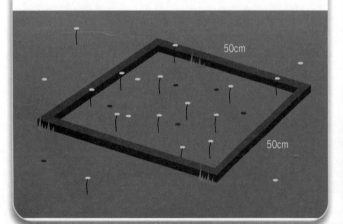

50cm

50cm

Identifying Organisms

You can look at plants and trap animals in pitfall traps, nets and pooters (a device that enables you to suck insects into a collection chamber without harming them). You can use keys to look up what the organisms are, then count and record the numbers.

A Pitfall Trap

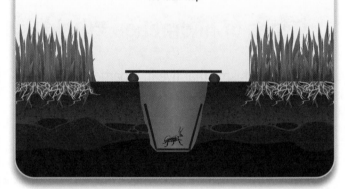

Measuring the Conditions

You can use different sorts of meters and data loggers to measure soil, water and air conditions, for example...
- a thermometer to measure temperature
- a light meter for light levels
- a flow meter for water flow
- a pH meter or universal indicator to measure the pH of soil.

This is preferably done over a period of time, not just in one go.

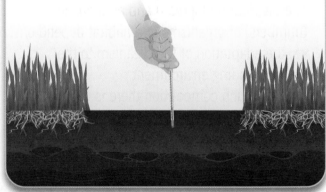

Food Chains

Once all the data has been collected, you can use the information to make **food chains** and food webs to show the feeding relationships in the habitat, for example:

Wheat   Harvest mouse   Owl

Energy in Food Chains

This is how energy would be passed along the food chain above:

- The wheat plants get their energy from sunlight. They use this energy for photosynthesis to make their own glucose. They also take in nutrients from the soil and use this to build their own proteins and fats, etc.

- Plants use up some of their glucose in respiration, which causes thermal (heat) energy to be given out into the surroundings. So, not all the energy produced by the plant is passed onto the harvest mouse.

- After eating the wheat, the mouse also respires, releasing heat. Some of this energy is used as kinetic (movement) energy. Some of the energy passes out from the mouse in urine and faeces. So, not all the energy from the mouse is passed onto the owl, and so on.

Numbers of Organisms

A lot of energy present in one step of the food chain isn't available to the animal in the next step. As a result...

- the number of organisms decreases dramatically from one feeding level to the next

- food chains are usually only three, four or five steps. There isn't enough energy left at the top to support another step.

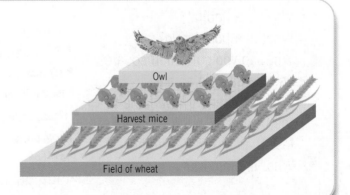

Owl

Harvest mice

Field of wheat

Environmental Relationships

Environmental Pyramids

Pyramid diagrams...

- help to show the numbers of **producers** (green plants), **primary consumers** (herbivores) and **secondary consumers** (first-level carnivores)
- give you an idea of how much energy is available at each feeding level and how it decreases as the food chain gets longer
- help you to compare different food chains to look at similarities and differences.

You can use a food chain and the number of organisms to produce a **pyramid of numbers**:

- The width of each bar shows the number of organisms and you usually get a typical pyramid shape **1**.
- Occasionally you get a strange-looking pyramid. For example, pyramid **2** is different because there is only one oak tree but many caterpillars eating its leaves. What this type of pyramid doesn't allow for is size.

In a **pyramid of biomass**, all the organisms are weighed and the total mass of each type of organism is calculated. The mass of the oak tree is far greater than the mass of all the caterpillars, so you get a typical pyramid shape again **3**.

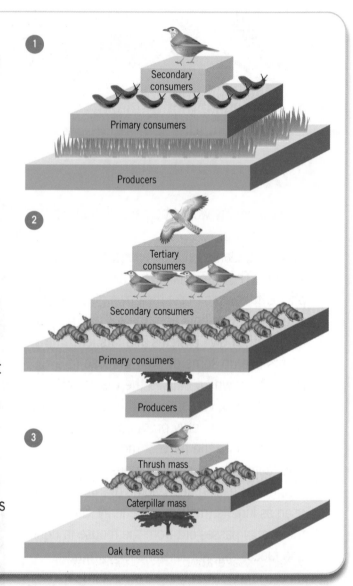

Quick Test

1. What is a habitat?
2. What is a population?
3. What do you call small squares used to sample an area?
4. Why is the energy available to the next step in a food chain less than at the beginning?
5. What is biomass?

Key Words Exercise

Match each key word with its meaning.

Key Word	Meaning
Biodiversity	The particular type of area in which an organism lives
Community	The total number of individuals of the same species in a habitat
Distribution	The total number of populations in a habitat
Ecosystem	The community of organisms together with the physical conditions in a defined area
Food chain	To move into an area
Habitat	The range of different species in an area
Immigration	The spread of individuals of a species in an area
Population	A device for sampling 'fixed' organisms in a large area
Primary consumers	A sequence of organisms showing 'what eats what' in an area
Producers	A way of showing the relative numbers of organisms in a food chain or web
Pyramid of biomass	A way of showing the relative mass of organisms in a food chain or web
Pyramid of numbers	A name given to green plants that can make their own food
Quadrat	A name given to animals that eat producers
Secondary consumers	A name given to animals that eat herbivores

Comprehension

Read the passage about food chains, then answer the following questions.

1. What is the name of the process by which producers convert light to chemical energy?

2. Why are rainforests more productive than deserts?

3. What are animals that eat producers called?

4. What are animals that eat other animals called?

5. How is most energy lost from each step of the food chain?

Sunlight energy sustains almost all the approximate two million species of organism on Earth. Producers can turn this light energy into chemical energy in the form of glucose.

Different ecosystems produce different amounts of chemical energy because they vary in the amount of light, water and nutrients available to them, and in factors such as temperature. Tropical rainforests are highly productive, while deserts are unproductive.

Animals eat the producers and, in turn, are eaten by other animals. In the process, energy that's stored in the bodies of each organism flows along a food chain. At each step, some energy is lost as heat in respiration, as kinetic (movement) energy and through excretion in urine and faeces. As a consequence, food chains rarely go beyond four or five steps.

Environmental Relationships

1 **Fill in the missing words to complete the sentences about environmental relationships.**

a) Animals and plants _____ to their environment, which increases their chances of _____ .

b) All the organisms living in a particular area are called a _____ .

c) You can use fieldwork to study the _____ of organisms in a _____ .

d) You can _____ a large area using a _____ to estimate the numbers of organisms.

e) A pyramid of _____ shows the total number of each organism in a food chain. A pyramid of _____ shows the mass of each organism in a food chain. This gives you some idea of the amount of _____ at each stage.

f) The total of all the organisms and the physical factors affecting an area is referred to as an _____ . You can measure the physical factors using instruments like a _____ for temperature or a _____ for light levels.

g) The number of animals can be estimated by using a method called capture-_____ .

2 **Study the environmental pyramids for the food chain below.**

grass ➡ rabbit ➡ fox

Numbers

| Fox |
| Rabbit |
| Grass |

Biomass

| Fox |
| Rabbit |
| Grass |

Now draw a pyramid of numbers and a pyramid of biomass for each of the following food chains:

a) broad bean ➡ blackfly ➡ blue tit ➡ sparrowhawk

b) dandelion ➡ mouse ➡ stoat ➡ fleas on stoat

A group of pupils used a net to catch stonefly nymphs at different points along a river. They began the sample on the edge of town.

Stonefly nymphs prefer water with high oxygen levels (unpolluted), so the pupils predicted that there would be more nymphs further away from the town.

The pupils used exactly the same method of capture at each point and took great care not to harm the animals as they did this. They recorded their results in the table below.

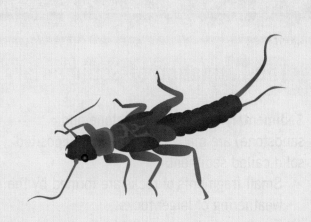

Sample Distance (metres from edge of town)	0	50	100	150	200	250
Number of Stonefly Nymphs	12	22	28	34	48	42

1. Plot the data onto a graph grid, labelling the axes clearly.

2. Which variables would the pupils have to assume would remain the same in order to make this investigation a fair test?

3. Which is the independent variable in this investigation?

4. Do these results support the pupils' prediction? Give a reason for your answer.

5. The result at 250 metres was lower than at 200 metres. Can you suggest a reason for this?

6. Why might the town make a difference to the number of stonefly nymphs?

The Rock Cycle

The Formation of Sedimentary Rocks

Sedimentary rocks (e.g. limestone and sandstone) are made from layers of **deposited** solid called sediment:

- Small fragments of rocks are formed by the weathering of larger rocks.
- The fragments are moved by rivers, glaciers and the wind, and are then deposited in layers.
- As more layers of sediment build up, the particles at the bottom are squeezed together.
- Water is squeezed out, leaving the dissolved salts that act as natural **cement**, gluing the grains together.
- Layers of sediment can also be formed when water that contains dissolved salts evaporates, leaving behind the salts as layers of sediment. These minerals (e.g. halite or 'rock salt') are called **evaporates**.

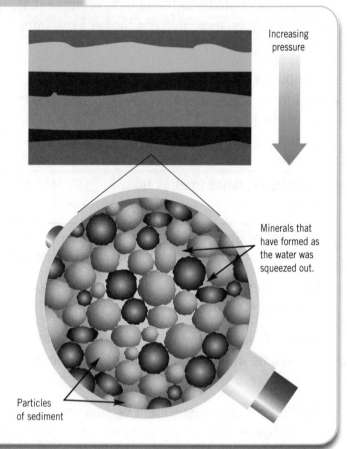

Increasing pressure

Minerals that have formed as the water was squeezed out.

Particles of sediment

Features of Sedimentary Rocks

Sedimentary rocks have these properties:

- They're quite soft and crumbly because the grains don't interlock.
- They may contain **fossils**, the remains of dead plants and animals that have been preserved in rocks.

Limestone   Sandstone

Limestone

Rocks rich in metal carbonates weather quickly when exposed to acidic rainwater:

Limestone, which contains calcium carbonate, is one type of rock that weathers quickly:

metal carbonate + acid ➡ salt + water + carbon dioxide

calcium carbonate + sulfuric acid ➡ calcium sulfate + water + carbon dioxide

The Formation of Metamorphic Rocks

Metamorphic rocks (e.g. **marble** and **slate**) are made when high temperatures and pressures change existing (usually sedimentary) rocks:

- Existing rocks are heated by molten rock called magma. As the rocks are heated, they recrystallise and new crystals are formed.
- Existing rocks are subjected to high pressures by forces in the Earth's crust or by the weight of rocks above them.

Original Rock	Metamorphic Rock
Mudstone	Slate
Limestone	Marble
Sandstone	Quartzite

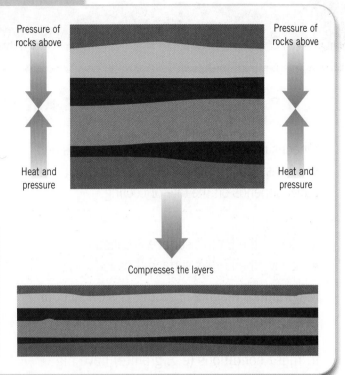

Pressure of rocks above

Heat and pressure

Pressure of rocks above

Heat and pressure

Compresses the layers

Features of Metamorphic Rocks

Metamorphic rocks have these properties:

- They're normally hard and shiny.
- They sometimes have bands of crystals.
- Different minerals form at different temperatures, so they can tell you how far the original rock was from the heat source that changed it.
- They occasionally contain fossils that have been deformed (changed) by low-level or 'low-grade' metamorphism. Higher level or 'high-grade' metamorphism can destroy the fossils completely.

Marble

Bands of Crystals in Gneiss

Folding and Faulting

When layers of rock are subjected to large forces, folding can be seen. Folding can create mountain chains, such as the Himalayas.

A fault occurs if the forces in the Earth's crust cause the layers of rock to fracture.

How Folding Affects Layers of Rock

Syncline	Anticline

The Rock Cycle

The Formation of Igneous Rocks

Igneous rocks form when molten rock cools and solidifies. The size of the crystals present in the rocks depends on the rate of cooling.

Molten rock...
- below the Earth's surface is called magma
- above the Earth's surface is called lava.

Magma in a magma chamber is slow to cool because there's a lot of it and it's well insulated by the surrounding rock. Igneous rocks formed in these conditions (e.g. granite) have big crystals because the slow rate of cooling gives plenty of time for the crystals to grow.

Magma can cut through rocks. The magma cools and solidifies into igneous rock. This shows the igneous rock is younger than the rock it cuts into.

At the Earth's surface, lava cools quickly because it's in contact with air or water. Igneous rocks formed in these conditions (e.g. basalt) have small crystals because the fast cooling gives less time for the crystals to grow.

Pumice is an igneous rock formed when volcanoes explode. Lava rich in volcanic gases is thrown out and it quickly solidifies to leave a rock that has lots of holes where the gases were.

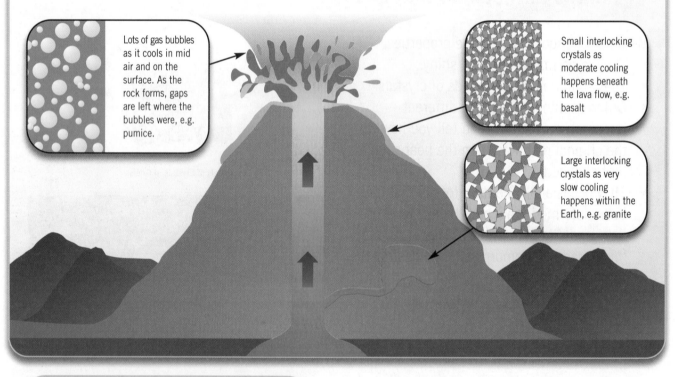

Lots of gas bubbles as it cools in mid air and on the surface. As the rock forms, gaps are left where the bubbles were, e.g. pumice.

Small interlocking crystals as moderate cooling happens beneath the lava flow, e.g. basalt

Large interlocking crystals as very slow cooling happens within the Earth, e.g. granite

Features of Igneous Rocks

Igneous rocks have these properties:
- They have interlocking crystals. This means that they're very hard and don't weather easily.
- They never contain fossils as the molten rock would destroy any organisms.

Basalt

Granite

The Rock Cycle

The rock cycle explains how the atoms in rocks are being recycled over long periods of time:

- When molten rock cools down and solidifies, igneous rocks are formed.
- Igneous rocks are weathered and the rock fragments are transported by rivers, glaciers or the wind. Eventually they're deposited.
- As the layers of sediment build up, the lowest layers are compressed and water is squeezed out. The grains become cemented together and sedimentary rocks are formed.

- Heat and pressure can change the sedimentary rocks and some igneous rocks, forming metamorphic rocks.
- If the temperature and pressure are increased further, the metamorphic rocks can melt completely to form magma.
- In this way, the atoms are being constantly recycled and an atom that is today in a sedimentary rock will, one day, be in a metamorphic rock or an igneous rock.

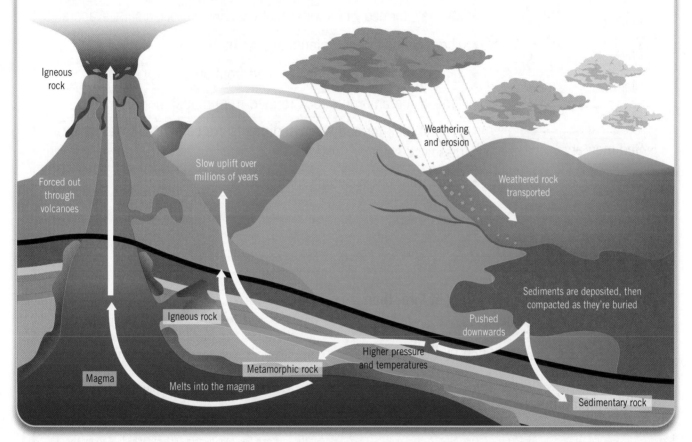

Igneous rock

Forced out through volcanoes

Slow uplift over millions of years

Weathering and erosion

Weathered rock transported

Sediments are deposited, then compacted as they're buried

Igneous rock

Pushed downwards

Magma

Metamorphic rock

Higher pressure and temperatures

Melts into the magma

Sedimentary rock

Quick Test

1. Which is the softest type of rock?
2. Name two things that can cause metamorphism?
3. Name the metamorphic rock formed from mudstone.
4. What is molten rock below the Earth's surface called?
5. What is molten rock above the Earth's surface called?
6. An igneous rock contains large crystals. Explain what this tells you about the formation of this rock.

KEY WORDS
Make sure you understand these words before moving on!
- Cement
- Deposit
- Evaporates
- Fossils
- Lava
- Magma
- Marble
- Sedimentary
- Slate

The Rock Cycle

Match each key word with its meaning.

Cement	Molten rock above the Earth's surface
Deposit	Molten rock below the Earth's surface
Evaporates	Lay down
Fossils	Minerals formed when water that contains dissolved salts evaporates
Lava	The remains of dead plants and animals
Magma	Type of metamorphic rock formed from limestone
Marble	Type of metamorphic rock formed from mudstone
Sedimentary	Type of rock formed when sediments are cemented together by dissolved salts
Slate	'Glue' that sticks sediments together

Comprehension

Read the passage about the Ring of Fire, then answer the following questions.

1. Which ocean is surrounded by the Ring of Fire?

2. Which features are associated with the Ring of Fire?

3. What is the centre of the Earth called?

4. How fast do the Earth's plates move?

5. How are earthquakes formed?

6. How are volcanoes formed?

Most of the world's earthquakes and volcanoes occur in a horseshoe-shaped band around the Pacific Ocean called the 'Ring of Fire'. Scientists have discovered that the Earth has a layered structure. At the centre of the Earth is the core. This is surrounded by a middle layer called the mantle. The outside layer, on which we live, is called the crust. The crust and the upper part of the mantle are split into about a dozen pieces called plates. These plates move across the surface of the Earth at the rate of a few centimetres per year, which is about the rate at which your finger nails grow.

The Ring of Fire marks the boundaries between many of these plates. The plates can move in three ways. They can move past each other, towards each other or away from each other. When the plates move past each other, they occasionally get stuck. Gradually, the forces build up until suddenly the plates move and the energy that had built up is released as an earthquake.

When the plates move towards each other, one plate is forced underneath the other. This results in volcanoes. When the plates move away from each other, magma comes to the surface. This normally happens under the sea and new sea floor is made. These plate movements result in the large number of earthquakes and volcanoes observed around the Ring of Fire.

Testing Understanding

1 **Fill in the missing words to complete the sentences about the rock cycle.**

a) Sedimentary _____ are formed from layers of sediment. As more layers build up, the _____ increases and water is squeezed out. The sediments are cemented together by the dissolved _____.

b) Sedimentary rocks, like sandstone and limestone, are quite soft and

_____.

c) Metamorphic rocks are formed when existing rocks are changed by high temperatures or high _____. Marble is made from _____ and slate is made from _____.

d) Metamorphic rocks are quite hard and shiny, and some have bands of

_____. Some low-grade metamorphic rocks may contain altered fossils, but the fossils are completely _____ in higher-grade metamorphic rocks.

e) Igneous rocks are formed when molten rock _____ down and solidifies. Molten rock below the surface of the Earth is called _____. It cools slowly to form _____ crystals.

f) Molten rock above the surface of the Earth is called _____. It cools more quickly to form _____ crystals.

2 **Study the boxes below, then answer the questions that follow.**

Type of Rock	Way it was Formed
Sedimentary	Grains of sediment are cemented together by dissolved salts
Metamorphic	Molten rock cools down and solidifies
Igneous	Existing rocks are changed by high temperatures and pressures

a) Link the type of rock to the way it was formed. Draw one line from each type of rock.
b) What is a fossil?
c) Which of these types of rock is most likely to contain fossils?
d) Which type of rock will never contain fossils? Explain your answer.

The Rock Cycle

Robyn has samples of four different igneous rocks. They are labelled A, B, C and D.

She measures the size of the crystals in each sample.

1 Name the piece of apparatus that Robyn could use to measure the size of the crystals in each sample.

Robyn's results are in the table below.

Rock Sample	Crystal Size (mm)
A	1
B	6
C	4
D	2

2 Use the information in the table to complete the graph opposite.

3 Use the graph to suggest which of these igneous rocks formed most slowly. Explain your answer.

4 Complete the table below to show the factor that Robyn changed, the variable that she measured and the variable that she kept the same in her experiment. Place one tick in each row.

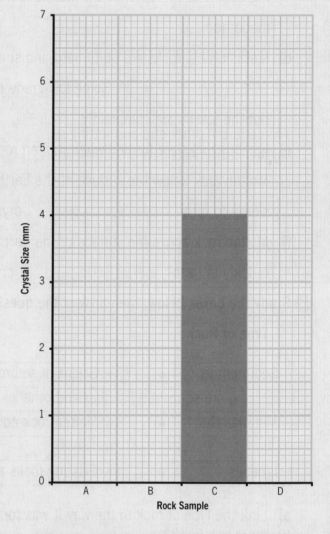

	Factor that was Changed	Factor that was Measured	Factor that was Kept the Same
Crystal Size			
Rock Sample			
Type of Rock that was Used			

Making Sound, Hearing Sound

Sound Waves

Sound, like light, is energy that travels in waves:
- Light waves are electromagnetic waves.
- Sound waves are mechanical waves.

Sound waves…
- are made by particles moving backwards and forwards in a wave motion
- carry energy from one place to another.

An object makes a sound wave when it vibrates:
- You can make a ruler vibrate over the edge of a desk by holding one end and applying a force to the other end and letting go.
- Musical instruments have vibrating parts – guitar strings vibrate and a drum skin vibrates.
- When you talk or sing, your vocal cords vibrate. You can feel them if you place your fingers gently against your throat.

Vibrations

A vibration is a repeating backwards and forwards motion of particles. As the particles vibrate, some are squashed together and others are spread apart.

Vibrations can travel through different materials, for example, through the air when you play a musical instrument:

- The instrument makes the air particles close to it vibrate and the vibrations are passed onto more air particles.
- When the vibrations reach your ears, you detect them as sound.

The air particles don't travel, they only vibrate. It's the sound waves that travel from the instrument to the ear.

The loud speaker vibrates right and left, squashing and stretching the air particles next to it.

The air particles vibrate and in turn cause other air particles to vibrate, passing along the squashing and stretching.

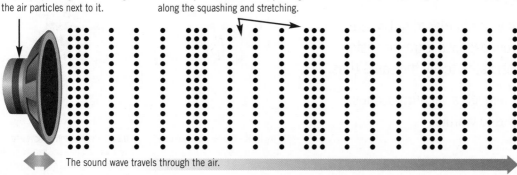

The sound wave travels through the air.

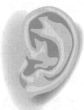

The ear detects the vibrations of the particles as sound.

Making Sound, Hearing Sound

The Human Ear

Sound waves are directed into the ear canal by the outer ear:

- The sound waves make the ear drum vibrate.
- These vibrations are passed onto the **cochlea** by a set of three small bones called the **hammer**, anvil and stirrup.
- In the cochlea, a liquid moves backwards and forwards and stimulates nerve cells, which send impulses to the brain through the **auditory nerve**.

The ears detect the direction that a sound is coming from by sensing which ear is closer to the sound.

Owls listen carefully with both ears to identify where a sound is coming from. Then they turn their head to make another measurement. This is how they can precisely locate their prey.

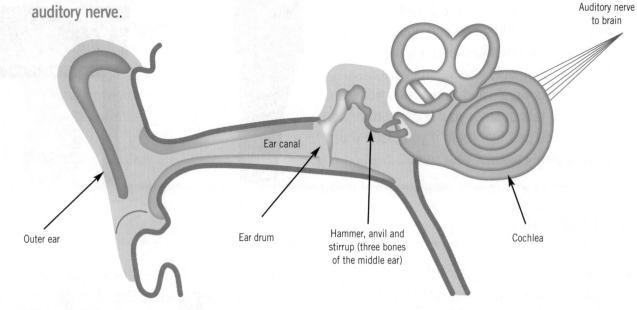

Auditory nerve to brain

Outer ear

Ear canal

Ear drum

Hammer, anvil and stirrup (three bones of the middle ear)

Cochlea

How Sound Travels

Sound travels through liquids and solids in the same way as it does through air, but it travels faster because the particles are closer together.

When you're in water, it's harder to tell where a sound is coming from because it travels faster and reaches both ears at virtually the same time.

Sound can't travel through a vacuum because there are no particles to vibrate.

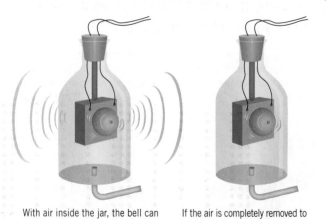

With air inside the jar, the bell can be heard and seen to be ringing.

If the air is completely removed to form a vacuum, the bell can be seen to be ringing but it can't be heard.

Frequency

The speed of the vibration of a sound wave is called the **frequency**:

- The unit of frequency is the Hertz or Hz.
- The frequency of a wave is the number of complete vibrations per second.
- Human ears can detect frequencies between 20Hz and 20 000Hz.
- The frequency affects the pitch of the sound. The higher the wave frequency, the higher the pitch.

Dolphins and whales can make sound waves of a wide range of frequencies, both lower and higher than your ears can detect. They use these sounds for hunting, navigating and communicating. Whales and dolphins communicate over many kilometres with very low frequency sound waves.

Using Sound Waves

Bats produce high frequency sounds, called ultrasound, in order to navigate. The bats detect the size and position of objects from the echoes produced by the sounds. The use of echoes to measure distances is called **echolocation**.

Echolocation can also be used on ships to measure the depth of water beneath them:

- A pulse of ultrasound is sent to the sea bed.
- The longer it takes for the echo to come back, the deeper the sea.

Ultrasound can also be used to...

- scan foetuses in the womb
- break up kidney stones without surgery
- clean surgical instruments.

A snake detects vibrations in the ground with the lower part of its jaw bone. The bone transmits the vibrations to its internal ears.

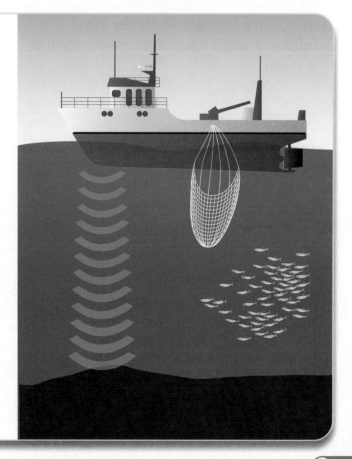

Making Sound, Hearing Sound

Describing a Wave

A sound wave vibrates particles to either side of their **rest position**. The distance the particles move each side, measured from their rest position, is called the **amplitude**.

You can't actually see sounds, but with a **microphone** connected to an **oscilloscope** you can see wave shapes on a screen. The microphone changes sound waves into electrical signals. The oscilloscope converts the signals into a moving wave shape on the screen called a waveform.

The **wavelength** is the distance from a point on a wave to the exact same point on the next wave (i.e. the length of one wave). High frequency sound waves correspond to high pitch notes and have shorter wavelengths.

The amplitude is the maximum distance the wave reaches from rest position. A sound wave with a large amplitude has a loud volume. A sound wave with a small amplitude is quieter.

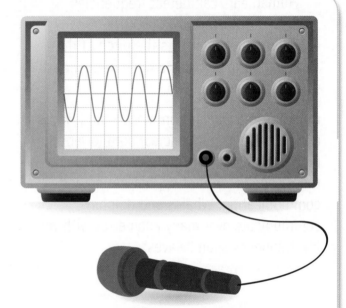

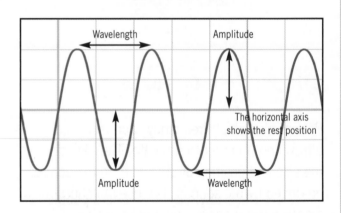

Quick Test

1. Sound waves are the vibration of particles. Do the particles move from one place to another?
2. What do sound waves carry from one place to another?
3. How does an owl identify where a sound is coming from?
4. Why can't sound travel through a vacuum?

Key Words Exercise

Match each key word to its meaning.

Key Word	Meaning
Amplitude	A coiled membrane full of liquid and nerve cells
Auditory nerve	The maximum distance from rest position
Cochlea	A sound wave can be viewed on one of these
Echolocation	This sends electrical impulses to the brain
Frequency	The number of complete waves per second
Hammer	A bone in the middle ear
Microphone	Measuring distances by detecting echoes
Oscilloscope	The normal position of a particle when it's not moving
Rest position	This converts sound energy into electricity
Wavelength	The distance between a point on a wave and the same point on the next wave

Comprehension

Read the passage about the dangers of noise, then answer the following questions.

1. What is the scientific name for a hole in the ear drum?

2. What permanent damage can be done inside the cochlea?

3. Name three environments where people can be exposed to loud noise.

4. How can people protect themselves from loud noises?

Exposure to a loud noise can cause damage to the ear drum, preventing it from vibrating efficiently, and hearing is lost. A hole in the ear drum, called a perforation, can sometimes heal and normal hearing can be restored.

However, if a person is exposed to loud noise over a long period of time, nerve endings in the cochlea can be damaged. This causes permanent loss of hearing. People who work in noisy environments, such as machinery workers, airport staff or members of music groups, are at risk from this kind of deafness. Ear protectors can be worn to reduce the amount of sound energy entering the ears.

Making Sound, Hearing Sound

Testing Understanding

1 **Fill in the missing words to complete the sentences about the human ear.**

a) Sound waves are directed into the ear _____ by the _____ ear.

b) Sound waves strike the ear _____, causing it to vibrate. These vibrations
are passed onto the _____ by a set of three small bones called the
hammer, anvil and _____.

c) In the cochlea, a liquid moves backwards and forwards and stimulates nerve
_____ inside it that send _____ to the brain through
the auditory nerve.

d) Your ears detect the _____ a sound is coming from by sensing which
_____ is closer to the sound.

e) You may have noticed in _____ that it's harder to identify where a sound
is coming from because the sound travels _____ and reaches both ears
at almost the same _____.

2 **Read the information about frequencies,
then answer the questions that follow.**

The highest frequency sound, or highest
pitch note, that a human can detect is
20 000Hz. Other animals can detect
sounds at much higher frequencies.

The graph opposite shows some of the
maximum frequencies that different
animals can hear.

a) What is meant by the frequency of a wave?

b) Which animals could hear a note of
frequency 85 000Hz?

c) Add to the graph the maximum
frequency a human can hear.

d) A dog whistle is used to call dogs. It can
be heard by dogs but not by humans.
Suggest a suitable frequency for the
note produced by a dog whistle.

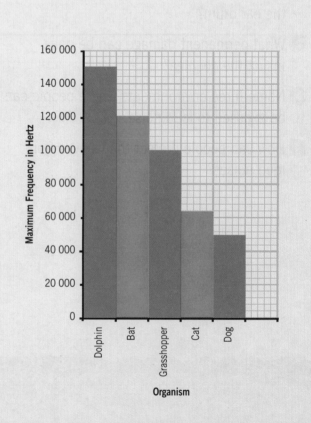

Mandy and Ivana want to use an oscilloscope to investigate different sounds. They want to compare the volume of different sounds with the amplitude of the waveform produced.

1 As well as an oscilloscope, what other piece of equipment do they need?

2 What is the amplitude of a wave?

Mandy has found a chart in a book that lists different sounds and their average loudness in decibels. She suggests that they could compare their results with the chart. The chart is shown below.

Sound	Loudness (decibels)
A whisper	25
Normal conversation	55
A hair dryer	60
A vacuum cleaner	80
Noisy traffic	80
A loud clap	90
A jet plane	125

3 Explain how Mandy and Ivana could use their equipment to measure the amplitude of a sound.

The results obtained in the experiment are recorded in the table below.

Sound	Amplitude on the Oscilloscope Screen (mm)
A whisper	10
Normal conversation	25
A hair dryer	25
A vacuum cleaner	35
Noisy traffic	45
A loud clap	60

4 Suggest how the girls could investigate whether there is a correlation between the sound levels in the chart and their results.

5 Carry out your suggestion to see whether there is a correlation or pattern between the two sets of results.

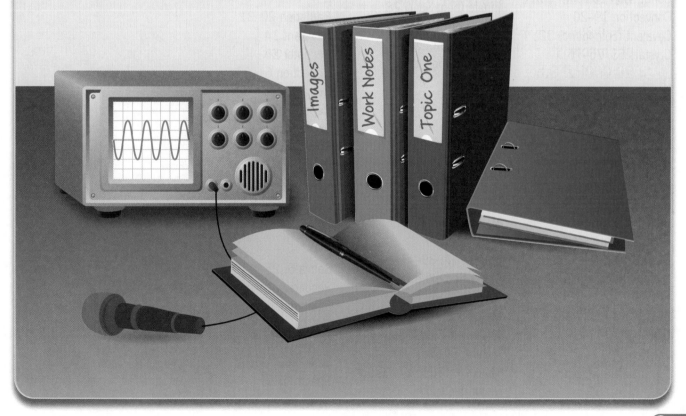

Index